LITTLE

Twelve years ago Bronwyn Hocking gave birth to Sam, a normal baby. As he grew, she gradually came to realize that he was not developing like a normal child. He also exhibited strange behaviour patterns and obsessions. Members of the medical profession were enigmatic in their observations, but eventually it became clear that Sam was autistic.

Little Boy Lost is about Sam and about Bronwyn Hocking's continuing quest to understand him and to communicate with him. The past twelve years have led her to question and examine what autism is and what causes it, and to examine herself with remarkable candour. The result is a brave and unsentimental story which leads to a controversial conclusion.

No one really understands autism – perhaps the loneliest affliction that any human has to endure – but Bronwyn Hocking has come closer than most to an explanation and to a possible course of action that can only bring hope to others.

Bronwyn Hocking was born and grew up in Australia. She came to live in the United Kingdom in her late teens, and after graduating from Hornsey Art College, she worked in London as a graphic designer and in the film industry. She then moved to Yorkshire, where she lived for ten years, working in television as a film editor and researcher. She and her son now live near Oxford. *Little Boy Lost* is her first book and was shortlisted for the 1990 Odd Fellows Book Award for a work highlighting an issue of social concern.

Little Boy Lost

BRONWYN HOCKING

BLOOMSBURY

First published in Great Britain 1990
Bloomsbury Publishing Limited, 2 Soho Square, London W1V 5DE
This paperback edition published 1991

A CIP catalogue record for this book
is available from the British Library

ISBN 0-7475-0955-7

10 9 8 7 6 5 4 3 2 1

Typeset by Hewer Text Composition Services, Edinburgh
Printed by Cox and Wyman Limited, Reading

This book is for my son, whose emotional scars are more crippling than mine ever were, but whose joy and pain I have chosen to share.

CONTENTS

	Preface	9
1	House on the Hill	11
2	The Baby	15
3	Initial Worries	21
4	Looking for Reasons	29
5	Nursery	41
6	Holding Therapy	53
7	School	70
8	All Alone	80
9	New Directions	91
10	New School	105
11	Conflict	118
12	Psychotherapy	126
13	Coming Alive	137
14	Shifting Sands	147
15	Language and Symbolism	156
16	Teaching and Learning	171
17	The Beginning at Last	182
	Epilogue	189
	Bibliography	191

NOTE

This book is a factual account of true events, and all the people described in these pages are real. However, some of the names have been changed in order to protect their privacy.

PREFACE

The story that I tell is a personal one. I clearly state that what I say is my own opinion regarding both the people and the relationships that I describe, the books that I discuss, and the conclusions that I reach about the nature and cause of autism.

Some people will disagree with my views about autism. The battle over the relative importance of nature versus nurture in the development of this condition has raged since autistic symptoms were first described by Leo Kanner in 1943. The dispute still continues today.

The theories that I first encountered were all based on the idea that autism is caused by some sort of biological or organic abnormality, possibly genetic in origin. This seemed to be the accepted view amongst the doctors and teachers with whom we came into contact. I eventually realized that although such ideas are generally accepted by the British medical profession, they carry less weight in some other European countries. In France and Italy, for example, there is more sympathy with the idea that autism is a psychological/emotional disability. This opens up a wide range of possibilities for treatment, especially if the condition is diagnosed early enough.

My own conclusions about autism reflect both my reading on the subject and my ten years of experience with my autistic son. I believe that the core from which all autistic behaviour grows is the autistic child's ongoing attempt to isolate himself from the experiences that for other people constitute the very stuff of life. He avoids relating directly to other people and he isolates himself from his environment. Even more destructive for him is his separation from his own feelings.

Cutting off from our emotions is something we all do sometimes.

We repress feelings with which we are unable to deal at a particular time. But autistic children use this protective device with such persistence, and from such a young age, that they do not develop the awareness of their own responses that provides the basis for future emotional development. With this first rung of the developmental ladder missing, successive steps are inevitably distorted, and many autistic children never develop the complex array of interdependent skills that are required for one person to interact with another.

There may be many reasons why a child fails to make and/or maintain meaningful contact with the world into which he is born, but one of them must surely be that his earliest experiences are not satisfying ones. Our society seems to shy away from this idea, in the mistaken belief that those who express such thoughts are trying to 'blame' parents for their children s problems. Blame is simply not relevant here. Parents have been children too, and may themselves have suffered in ways that make it difficult for them to relate to their own children. The fault for such a sad sequence of events belongs to nobody. The consequences are borne by the child, the mother and the family, and by the society that fails to take account of the importance of first acknowledging how tragically things can go wrong in our relations with our children, and then helping parents to repair them when they do.

1

HOUSE ON THE HILL

As 1978 drew to a close, one of the coldest winters for many years was just coming to life. Sharpening teeth and claws, it prepared for the onslaught. By the time my son was born, just into the New Year, the winter had really begun to bite. Blizzard winds whistled through the rafters and rattled the rotting window frames of our tiny stone cottage. Icicles hung three feet deep across the windows. Our magical view across the valley was obscured for months, and at times we were completely snowbound. This was the beginning of our isolation.

Peter and I had moved to Yorkshire from London several years earlier, but only recently into our cottage. We had neither friends nor relatives in the area, and were very involved – too involved – with each other. The house was at the end of a terrace of four, one of three terraces grouped together in the middle of open countryside in typical Yorkshire fashion. There was a solitary shop and in some ways the social environment resembled that of a small village, with the nearest town several miles away. The village hugged the north-facing slope of a steep ridge, part of the first undulation of hills that as it gathered momentum became the Yorkshire Dales. Our cottage was indeed 'delightfully situated', but peeling wallpaper and rising damp made its 'great potential' seem a long way from realization.

The house had been empty for years, waiting for a pair of innocents like Peter and me to come along. We fell in love with the view – I had always wanted to live on a hill – and with the overgrown mess of a garden. From the first time that we saw the house I wanted to buy it, even though we had no key and could not get inside to look around. But Peter was less sure. He did not tell me until years later, but something happened that day that bothered him.

As we were walking away Peter had turned back for a last look, and there in the upstairs window a bird had been flapping, trapped and frantic. We found it when we did eventually get inside on our next visit. It was dead. A small pile of dirty feathers lying on the curling linoleum. I do not think that I would even have noticed had Peter not pointed it out to me. But whether he dismissed what had seemed a bad omen as foolishness on his part, or whether he was simply won over by my enthusiasm, Peter soon came round to the idea of buying Valley View. We rushed headlong into our new venture, wildly excited by the idea of ownership and consequent freedom from landlords, and quite undaunted by the prospect of having to 'do up' what was in reality an uninhabitable shell. We had no idea what was involved – some sanding and hammering, we thought, with perhaps a man to help out occasionally on some of the bigger jobs. We had no furniture, no heating or hot water, no floor coverings and in one room no floor at all – just bare earth below rotting timbers. Neither did we have any financial resources. We were very naïve.

Two things stand out in my memory of those first few months in our frost-bitten cottage: the misery of continual cold and the joy of owning my own home. The joy was the greater of the two, and sustained us through the dawning awareness that what we had done was not very sensible. We should certainly have remained in our flat until some of the more basic repairs, at least, had been effected. The evenings were the worst, because we were frozen by then, and usually hungry. Our slender resources did not stretch to much beyond the bare essentials, so it was bread and potatoes with endless cups of tepid tea. The water would not boil and the potatoes would not cook on our eighty-year-old Yorkshire range. It was a handsome object, but just did not seem to work. Peter and I struggled with the perversities of firebox and flues night after night for eighteen months, until at last we tore it out and smashed it to pieces in a fit of gleeful revenge.

Keeping warm was a problem, so despite the stresses and cracks that had begun to appear in our relationship we still huddled together. We clung to each other, desperate for security and trying to extract from each other what we each felt to be lacking in ourselves. Sometimes we succeeded. Sometimes we were very happy indeed.

We had been four months in Valley View, and the elusive green haze hanging over the birch-tree wood had established itself as a new coat of fresh green leaves, when I found that I was pregnant. Although not totally unexpected, the idea of having a baby threw us both into a state of confusion. I had been doing freelance work for several months, but Peter had gone back into full-time employment only a week before I made my discovery. The timing was precarious to say the least.

As well as the demands imposed by his new job, Peter I think felt deep anxiety about his ability to provide for me and our child, and also about the unknown quantity of a child sharing our lives. We were not married, although we had been together for many years, and this worried me during those early months of my pregnancy. I felt alone and vulnerable. We always intended to get round to doing it, but somehow never did, and then later on it seemed too late.

Physically my pregnancy proceeded smoothly, but mentally I was in a state of turmoil. I was deeply concerned about the inadequacy of our house. It was cold, draughty and unfurnished and did not feel like a suitable home for a new-born baby. I was also anxious about my relationship with Peter, who seemed either remote or volatile and unpredictable. Then of course I had the usual worries about my child's being deformed or handicapped in some way. But it was worse than that. I somehow felt that a child of mine could not actually exist, a feeling that was reinforced by the negative attitudes of my sisters towards my pregnancy. They both lived a long way off, so communication was by telephone only. The elder of my two sisters assured me that I would not be a fit mother and should certainly have an abortion, while the second one concluded from her 'cherry-stone test' that my child was of an indefinable sex, which made him seem strangely non-existent. These assertions worried me greatly.

My sisters are both much older than I am. Being teenagers when I was born, they had seen at first hand the effect that my mother's resentful antagonism had on my development, and perhaps sensed instinctively that I would run into difficulties if I tried to bring up a child of my own. They were right – but their predictions of doom did me no good at all, ignorant as I then was of the events on which they were based.

I left work when I was about six months pregnant, and then for emotional reasons rather than out of physical necessity. Being at work was a strain, because even though my job with a television company was reasonably interesting I could not relate to the people around me. In those days I was a very anxious person. Peter's new job was in the same department as mine, and when he started working in the room next door my working environment seemed even more stressful. I was glad of an excuse to leave it.

Having severed this link with the outside world and being without friends or neighbours of my own age to talk to, I was now on my own almost all of the time. The fact that I was totally dependent upon Peter, both financially and emotionally, frightened us both. He was enjoying a certain amount of success and working long hours, so our time together was limited to brief meetings in the mornings and late at night when he got home. He probably began to feel that work was a more agreeable place to be than home, which although no longer the frozen icebox that it had been, could still not be described as anything other than spartan. Peter's absence and my condition meant that the restoration of our cottage proceeded frustratingly slowly.

As my pregnancy advanced, my state of mind deteriorated. I could not even concentrate on reading. The stress involved in appearing to be 'all right' was enormous, as I made a great effort to hide my fears from neighbours and from my doctor. I might have cracked under the strain had it not been for the fact that I made a friend. Meeting Jo eased things considerably. She had recently moved into the terrace just along from ours, and our babies were due at about the same time. We met at our antenatal class, where we both felt ourselves to be misfits. Our situations were in some respects similar as, being in our thirties, we were both 'older' first-time mothers. We spent time together and found that we had much in common. This reassured me. Jo did not seem to think that Peter's violent outbursts were alarming or that my neurotic behaviour was in any way unusual. Perhaps she did not notice. But violent he was, and neurotic I was. It was into this environment that our son was born.

2

THE BABY

To my great distress, Sam's birth was induced. I had intended to have my baby in our small local maternity unit, but things did not work out that way. I was sent to the main hospital in town for a check-up. There I was told that I must stay in because my blood pressure was raised – owing, I felt, to the fact that I had been lying half naked under a sheet for two hours when it was tested. National Health medical practice prevailed, however, and I was whisked into a ward. After fretting there for several days I was eventually told that my child's birth was two weeks overdue. This was news to me, but I was assured that it was so. A midnight dash to the delivery room turned out to be a false alarm. Then, after several hours during which not much happened, an ominous-looking drips trolley appeared in the doorway. The baby had to be induced, it seemed. I did not want to risk his being harmed, did I? 'No of course not, but . . .'

My protests were ignored, which did not surprise me. I felt that fate had now assumed control; our future lay in the lap of the gods. And so Sam was induced. It was a frightening experience. Despite the waves of agony that passed through my body, hour after hour, I felt strangely non-existent. Then chaos descended. People began shouting, 'Push, push,' emphatically, urgently. This was my cue. I fumbled with the tattered shreds of my memory, but the proper response to the instruction eluded me. I could not remember anything. The pain reached a crescendo, then it was all over. A few minutes later a warm bundle landed in my arms for a few minutes, then disappeared. So did everybody else.

When several hours later I was still lying alone in the delivery room, it had begun to feel as though the rest of my life would be spent in that cold, empty place. At last a scrap of information fluttered down through my consciousness, as a passing nurse informed me that I must wait for my child to be seen by a paediatrician. 'Why?' I wondered. It was by that time 2 a.m. I was lonely and confused, and did not know where my baby was. Sadly I mourned the difference between the events of the last twenty-four hours and the fulfilling experience in a relaxed and happy atmosphere that I had hoped for.

The next two days passed in a blur, until we eventually reached our original destination, the maternity unit in our local hospital. The atmosphere there was friendly, and the ward less crowded, but my son and I had got off to a bad start. I was encouraged to breast-feed him and wanted to do so, but it did not happen naturally and easily in the way that I had expected. Every four hours we mothers sat by our beds, babes in arms, and put them to the breast. 'One minute each side for four minutes,' the nurse rapped cheerfully. Dutifully I went through the motions, but noted that Sam never sucked for more than a few seconds at a time. At first this worried me considerably, and I mentioned it once or twice, but after that I just pretended not to notice. 'It must be all right,' I thought, and proceeded with what I now believe to have been a very bad feeding pattern. Putting Sam to the breast became a source of great anxiety to me, and I shielded myself from the hopelessness that I felt when he did not suck by cutting myself off from my feelings. Not for us the 'reciprocal interaction' described by D.W. Winnicott in *The Maturational Processes and the Facilitating Environment*. I quote a passage that impressed me particularly as an illustration of what we did not do:

Imagine a baby who has never had a feed. Hunger turns up, and the baby is ready to conceive of something; out of need the baby is ready to create a source of satisfaction, but there is no previous experience to show the baby what to expect. If at this moment the mother places her breast where the baby is ready to expect something, and if plenty of time is allowed for the infant to feel around, with mouth and hands, and perhaps with a sense of smell, the baby 'creates' just what is there to be found. The baby eventually gets the illusion that this real breast is exactly the thing that was created out of need, greed, and the first impulse of primitive loving. Sight, smell and taste register somewhere, and after a while the baby may be creating something like the very breast that the mother has to offer. A thousand times the feeling has existed that what was wanted was created, and found to be there. From this develops a belief that the world can contain what is wanted and needed, with the result that the baby has hope that there is a live relationship between inner reality and external reality, between innate primary creativity and the world at large which is shared by all.

When I came across the work of this inspirational child psychologist, many years later, I wept bitter tears of pain and frustration at the joy that my son and I had missed, the deprivation that he had suffered, and the sheer futility of human potential without the first basic building-blocks for personal development. I realized that Sam and I had been unlucky. Whether or not my unhappy pregnancy affected my unborn child adversely, the circumstances surrounding his birth certainly added considerably to the stress that he suffered during that earliest part of his life. This meant that the first rung of his developmental ladder was weakened, which increased the likelihood of his stumbling upon the next step should it prove to be less than perfectly placed. So because Sam's first experience of the world was difficult, I think that it made him vulnerable.

My last few days in hospital were filled with trepidation. I had dreadful nightmares, being torn between the desire to get back home, to check that everything was all right, and fear that when I got there I would not be able to cope. Peter had been acting strangely, apparently unable to remember the visiting hours in the ward and usually tearing in, panic-stricken, just as everybody else was leaving.

'You're late, it's time to leave. You'll have to go in a minute,' I would reproach.

'But it's just four. You said four until five,' he would defend.

'I don't understand. You did this yesterday. Why can't you come on time like everybody else?'

'Sorry. Sorry. I'm really sorry.'

I would cry, Peter would look crestfallen. And so it went on for the duration of my stay in hospital.

At last it was time for Sam and me to leave the maternity unit, and Peter was there to take us home. It was four degrees below freezing the morning we stepped out into the world, but beautiful beyond belief. Though it was too cold for snow, the roads and trees sparkled with frost, brilliant in the sunshine. We gingerly wedged the carrycot into the back seat, hardly daring to look at its contents.

'Is he all right?' asked Peter.

'Yes,' I said, 'he's all right.'

At home we drank the champagne on which Peter had spent the last of our money. We gazed in awe at our son, still asleep in the carrycot between us. As the heavenly strains of Delius's *A Walk in the Paradise Garden* wafted across the valley below me, I remember catching for the first time a sudden glimpse of the enormity of what we had done.

The new reality soon became established. Tiredness affected my every waking moment, like a sprinkling of grey dust over everything. Night and day merged into a continuous desire for sleep, interspersed with periods of blissful oblivion which would be abruptly terminated by my crying infant. I felt unable to meet his continual demands and could not understand why he never stopped crying. His needs seemed infinite, my resources meagre. Although unaware of the fact then, I realized later that he was probably hungry most of the time, for we never did establish a proper feeding pattern. His weight gain was low, and during one period he actually lost weight.

A month later my friend Jo's son, Harry, was born, and from then on we had each other to lean on. It soon became apparent, to me at least, that I was leaning more than she was. Although Jo found the responsibility of caring for a dependent being hard to bear after her life of total independence and a successful career, she did at least have friends and relatives for support. Feeling that I lacked such back-up I envied her, but was grateful that she was there. We used to lie our babies on the carpet in her front room and watch and compare them as we drank coffee. Sam was long and thin, Harry short and round. There was never any question about there being anything wrong with Sam. In fact I remember feeling sorry for Jo because her baby had a small hernia, which, although it healed quickly, made him seem less than perfect for those first few weeks – or so it seemed to my critical eye. Ironically, as it turned out, Sam appeared to be the more sociable of the two; he used to reach out for Harry's hand and look him straight in the eye. I would not rely upon my own memory of such distant events, but I have photographs of Sam clasping Harry's hand and smiling full into his face.

Sam was described by my health visitor as a twitchy baby. I remember that he had an odd way of shaking his head sometimes, like a little old man. Apart from this eccentricity, however, his developments seemed to proceed normally. He smiled at five weeks, gazed at his twiddling fingers and toes, and got very excited about patterns and textures. He seemed almost over-responsive to some forms of stimulation and would shake all over at the sight of a particular shape or pattern that he liked.

During this time Peter and I were continually working on the house. There was so much to be done, and although we now had enough money to buy the materials that enabled us to undertake mammoth jobs ourselves, we could not afford to pay anybody to help us. We proceeded in a haphazard sort of way, taking pleasure in some of our more successful projects, despairing over others, and arguing constantly about everything. Although Sam still cried upon waking each morning he seemed content to lie in his pram while we worked. Often he would spend much of his day parked under the lilac tree in our garden, watching the leaves fluttering overhead. He rarely complained, so we assumed that he was happy and that the way he behaved was the way all children behaved. Not so our health visitor. She said that at six months Sam should be reaching for objects, and gently suggested that we try to interest him in doing so by making a game of it. But this did not come naturally to either Peter or me.

It had seemed to me such a small thing to quibble over – whether a child would reach for a bunch of keys or not – but when several weeks later I heard a radio programme about autism, I did begin to wonder. It struck me forcefully that all the words used to describe the condition applied precisely to my son, though I had not thought him to be anything other than normal. He did not look at me as I moved about and he did not seem curious enough to reach out for things. But even feeling that Sam's behaviour had much in common with that described as autistic did not worry me unduly. Not knowing what autism was, I imagined it to be a rather curious, romantic sort of condition that affected very intelligent children. I thought no more about it. Then Sam went for his eight-month hearing test, and failed. He just did not respond. That really worried me. I thought, 'My God, he's deaf, he's handicapped,' and I was alarmed. He had three more hearing tests at the local clinic, but I got the feeling that in the end they just gave up, mystified. He seemed to hear some things, but not others. The slightest trickle of water filled him with wild delight, but a large saucepan being dropped behind him caused not a flicker of reaction. Autism was never mentioned. I stopped worrying.

When Sam was nine months old we went on holiday to the seaside with some friends who also had children. My friend Ann thought that Sam was lovely, which made me very happy, and she was sure that there was nothing wrong with him. Sam really opened up during our two weeks in Cornwall. In the cheerful holiday atmosphere Peter and I relaxed and enjoyed ourselves. No doubt Sam responded to our happier mood, as well as to having other people around him.

Our last holiday morning dawned sunny and beautiful. A delicious salty breeze skidded across the coastline, and the green and brown streaked cliffs descending into the sea still took my breath away. I could not bear the thought of leaving. In fact we did try to extend our stay; it was as though both Peter and I sensed that this was the end of something for ever. But we had to go. We took a last lingering walk along the cliff tops, said our goodbyes, then headed back north for home. It had been a wonderful holiday – and the last time that I was ever to be free from worry about my son.

3

INITIAL WORRIES

As the days drew in and the leaves fell, my heart sank. It was chilly and misty in the afternoons now when I took Sam for his walk through the woods. He seemed to like these outings, though he never made any attempt to venture from the safety of his pushchair. Although I enjoyed them too, there was very little communication between us. This bothered me, but the more I worried about it, the more I tried not to think. I was depressed and lonely, for Jo had now moved away and was busy settling into her new house. Also, she had become pregnant again, which in my unhappy state I felt to be a betrayal as it meant that we were no longer in the same boat.

It sometimes seemed as though Sam and I were the only two people on earth. Peter was hardly ever at home, and when he was, appeared miserable and angry. I could not understand why, and he did not seem to either. Earlier in the year he had had an affair, which had left me feeling emotionally battered and very insecure. The more he hurt me, the more I turned to him for comfort, for there was no one else. It was a vicious circle. And yet we both loved Sam. We wanted to be a happy family, and sometimes things would settle down for a while. We sometimes had lovely days together. Peter could be a most loving father, and perhaps the happiest times that he and Sam had together were those when he would sit Sam upon his shoulders and take him for long treks through the countryside. They would not return until many hours later, by which time Sam would be exhausted, but wildly excited.

As we slid into winter, anxiety took a firm hold of me. At ten months Sam was only just sitting up on his own. I remember trying to explain my worries to my sister on the telephone, but it was difficult to define what was wrong with my son. He seemed to lack assertiveness, yet not curiosity. Peter was also concerned now, and devised his own test for Sam. He sat him on the floor in the middle of a circle of interesting-looking objects and toys. Sam hardly even looked at them, let alone reached out. Yet some visual phenomena still excited him to the extent that he would be thrown into paroxysms of delight: he would quiver all over at the sight of a light, or a pattern of letters on the side of a packet. It seemed that although Sam would seldom take the initiative himself, his response to experiences that were visited upon him was extreme.

The health visitor expressed concern at Sam's slow development, but our general practitioner said that he was fine. 'Just within normal limits,' he said, 'nothing to worry about.' The winter dragged on. I quote from a diary that I kept at that time:

Sam is just over a year now. I have been finding it difficult with him lately. Although I love him it is very frustrating being so tied to another human being and not being able to do things. I feel so full of energy and long to do huge physical tasks, but I am obliged to stay in this room and look after him. I know that I am utterly selfish, and foolish as well, waiting for him to grow older when this time with him as a baby is so short and will seem precious later. It does too, sometimes. Sam is a bit late doing things – sitting up, teething, crawling, walking (he's not doing this yet), and talking. I can't wait for him to talk so that we can communicate with each other. I'm sure that I will feel better when we can do that. It seems important that Sam should learn to do things quickly, but of course it is not really. Sometimes I feel that his social responses are very mature. He seems to exhibit a wide range of moods. He takes sidelong glances at things, and on occasion I am sure that he is trying to joke with me.

But one thing that does concern me is the way that it is impossible to catch his attention – by *any* means. I have tried clapping and shouting, which is all to no avail unless he is in a sociable mood. He also shows little motivation to overcome obstacles. He seems fascinated and excited, and always has done, by patterns and textures.

I must alter my attitude towards him in the daytime when we are alone here together. Perhaps it is just a matter of slowing myself down. I must enter his world instead of resenting the fact that he cannot enter mine. We would both be happier if I could do this. Sam responds very much to the amount of attention that he receives. He becomes withdrawn when I don't pay him enough of it, and he needs a great deal. But he never asks. He does not shout for things in the way that Harry does, he just becomes sad when left alone too long. This has a cumulative effect, so that after a week or so I begin to think of him as a quiet little thing who never does respond. But if on the other hand I give him plenty of attention (as both Peter and I did today) he becomes much more gregarious. In fact at times he has seemed incredibly so.

During that interminable winter I did little other than write in my diary. Then one rare sunny day in February I was sitting outside with Sam when I looked up to see Jo and Harry coming up the path. I was delighted. I had not seen Jo since she moved away five months before, in fact I had hardly seen anybody in that time. We went inside for coffee and set the babies together on the floor, as we used to do. Suddenly Harry moved off in a scampering sort of way. I was astonished. 'What is he doing?' I asked.

'He's crawling,' said Jo. 'He's been doing that for months.' And she laughed.

Of course. Harry was fourteen months old. Of course he would be crawling. But Sam wasn't. He could still only just sit up. The difference between the two children was considerable and I could not help commenting.

'Don't worry about it,' said Jo. 'They're all different. They don't all develop at the same rate. Anyway, what difference does it make?'

But it made a difference to me, and it went on making a difference long after Jo and Harry had gone. To make it worse we had taken photographs that day. Sam's face was red and puffy – something I later discovered was caused by his allergies – and his distant expression clearly showed his lack of involvement with his surroundings. The evidence of the difference between the two children was there in the pictures. They were a continual reminder from which I could not escape, taunting me from my bottom drawer where I had hidden them. Too afraid of worrying him to show them to Peter, I thought, 'I'll just leave them there until Sam has caught up; then I will show him.'

I still had not shown them to Peter a few months later when the health visitor expressed definite concern about Sam's development. She couched it in terms designed not to alarm me, but I was so withdrawn by this time that nothing worried me. Although I was in a constant state of depressed agitation, nothing really bothered me more than anything else. Everything was pushed down into the thick soup of anxiety which bubbled continuously on my back burner. The idea of Sam being 'substandard' was unthinkable; I needed him to be superhuman. However, she insisted that I take my son to our GP again, and this visit evoked a very different response from the previous one. Sam was now pronounced to be slow in his development and no longer reaching his milestones.

Several tests were carried out at the local hospital. These revealed nothing, so it was arranged for us to visit the child development unit of the main hospital in town. We were to attend a weekly session there with a play therapist, who would try to stimulate Sam while at the same time making an assessment of his potential.

As we sat waiting for the first session I was gripped by fear, terrified of finally being told that there was something wrong with my son.

The room was low-ceilinged and modern, light and airy. There were pictures of animals on the walls and a large wooden play-house. The woman sitting opposite me was enormously fat, her girth increased still further by the various carrier-bags, jackets, toys and assorted jumpers that she carried about her person. She looked dishevelled and weary. Of her three children only the youngest, the one who was handicapped, appeared to be under her control. He was afflicted by what I later recognized to have been cerebral palsy. At the time he just seemed to be terribly handicapped. I was not very familiar with children, and her other two seemed strange, incomprehensible beasts. I could not decide whether they had anything wrong with them or not. I felt deep pity for this woman and for the other parents who like me waited silently to be called. Their children all had obvious problems and I desperately needed to feel that Sam did not, and that we were not like them. Sam was immature and somewhat vague but he still looked 'normal' – and was, at that time, comparatively so.

Sally, the play therapist, was a bright, cheerful woman who seemed undaunted by Sam's apathy. As I sat watching her attempts to stimulate my child into action – any action – I occasionally experienced moments of acute pleasure. The sight of somebody trying to communicate with him filled me with an inexpressible joy, and when he occasionally responded I could have wept. The play therapy may have helped Sam; at least I am sure that it did him no harm. But I really needed it; for me it was a lifeline. It was the only time during the week that I came into contact with other people, and it drew me sharply back to the reality that I was a mother, that this was my child, and that I must try to understand and look after him.

After about six months of individual sessions it was suggested that Sam join one of the small groups of children having therapy sessions at the child development unit. I was apprehensive about this. I did not think that any child could begin to negotiate the complexities of relating to a group without first having the firm anchor of a relationship with one person – which I felt that Sam had been beginning to form with Sally. But I had no confidence in my own thoughts or abilities, and also laboured under the misapprehension that those around me knew what they were doing and had some ultimate plan for helping my son. Sam joined the group – in body if not in spirit. Thereafter any benefit that he had been deriving ceased – or that was my impression as I watched him wandering aimlessly amongst the other children or staring absently into space.

Eventually an appointment was made for us to talk with the chief psychologist, who had the unenviable task of trying to explain to parents like us the nature and consequences of their children's problems. I sat nervously on the edge of my seat, anxiously awaiting the judgement which I expected would determine the whole course of our future. Dr Jones rifled distractedly through the papers on his desk, as if searching there for the answer. He did not find it. It seemed that it was difficult to say what was wrong with Sam, and difficult to give a prognosis. He had 'autistic traits', but that did not mean that he was autistic. Did we really want a label, Dr Jones queried?

'Not particularly,' I said, 'I just want to know what is wrong with my son.'

'Well, this sort of autistic type of problem is very hard to pinpoint, difficult to categorize,' Dr Jones informed us.

In his opinion (which I took as gospel then), it was to do with maturation of the brain. Different bits were maturing at different rates, apparently, making the whole thing lopsided, and Sam's development uneven. Things might improve as Sam got older; on the other hand they might not. Who was to know?

Peter and I left feeling confused and frustrated. A straight 'We do not know what causes these problems but different professionals hold differing views – here are some of them' might have been more helpful. It would certainly have revealed the true situation more clearly to us.

At this point we decided to join the National Society for Autistic Children, which was the officially acknowledged support group for parents of autistic children in England. It seemed a large and well established society which ran a network of schools throughout the country and was represented by self-contained local groups. From the reading list they sent to me I got hold of several accounts of autistic children and began to realize that Sam was not unique in his peculiar behaviour. As I read the list of diagnostic symptoms I was torn between feeling relief at the discovery that here at last was a category into which my son fitted, and the chilling recognition that this was a devastatingly severe condition which would affect the whole of his development. Resistance to change, lack of language development, lack of effective contact with other people, a fascination with objects, abnormal responses to sensory experiences – Sam had the lot. But it was reassuring to find that there were other people in our position, and at least to feel that now I was doing something. I knew that I had a problem, and expended much energy in pursuit of knowledge regarding its nature and cause. I read Lorna Wing's *Autistic Children: A Guide for Parents*, and talked to other parents on the telephone. One such parent, Elaine, who ran the local Autistic Society group, came to visit me with her autistic son. He had the same ethereal quality that Sam possessed. Experiences had not etched the lines of expression upon this child's face, any more than they had upon Sam's. I could see many similarities between the two boys, and from this time the idea that my son was autistic gradually began to grow.

Yet I felt that the literature that I was reading was somehow failing to give me any real understanding of this puzzling condition. It was about symptoms and behaviour, and possibilities and likelihoods. There was no linking together of symptoms to form an overall theory of cause and effect that came anywhere near to explaining my son's strange behaviour.

And one thing still haunted me like a ghostly spectre which was forever just out of focus. I had always had the inexplicable feeling that something was dreadfully wrong between Sam and myself. I did not know what it was, or why it should be so. Having no other children I could draw no comparisons. I looked after Sam, bathed and dressed him, fed and changed his nappies, but I never really looked *at* him. And he did not look at me. We co-existed like two planets in space, spinning round each other, yet not touching. Inextricably tied to each other, yet prevented by forces beyond our control or understanding from escaping the isolation in which we both lived. Of course Sam was now said to have autistic traits, so he could be expected to have difficulty relating to people. But I knew that it was not just that. I could not relate to him any better than he could to me.

I tried to explain my feelings about the lack of any real relationship between us to people at the child development unit, but nobody seemed to take me seriously. It is strangely disorientating to be told by a psychologist that you are imagining that you cannot relate to your child. He was convinced that the problems lay with my son, and that my worries were nothing more than a manifestation of my inability to come to terms with the fact that he was handicapped.

Perhaps the psychologist drew his conclusions from Sam's appearing to be well looked after and having no bruises. We were not classified as an 'at risk' family. Had the psychologist been able to spend half an hour as a fly on the wall in our living room, he might well have come to think differently. But I obviously failed to communicate effectively my distress, or the reasons for it, and I must admit that part of me was trying hard to conceal the fact that we were in trouble. I could not bear the idea of anyone seeing the emotional mess in which Peter and I lived, and in which our child was expected to develop. For this reason, my cry for help must have been muffled and distorted and I do not suppose that anyone could have heard it. Certainly no one did – not then anyway.

It became apparent that the group session that Sam attended at the unit was not helping him, and so it was suggested that we might try him at a local day nursery for a couple of hours each week. Although there was a long waiting list, the matron agreed to let us start coming immediately one afternoon per week, as long as I would stay with Sam. I was delighted that he would be doing something normal at last, with normal children.

I later understood that the nursery was dreadfully understaffed and underfunded, but at the time it seemed to me a wonderful place. The atmosphere was friendly, and I was fascinated by the way that the other children so obviously learned things from each other through the medium of ordinary communication. But most of the time Sam either sat close to me or indulged in obsessive activities, like spinning the wheels of a car or twiddling the edge of a piece of cloth.

There were times, however, when I caught sight of him watching the other children, almost surreptitiously, and as gradually I became aware of how great a part involvement with other people plays in a child's development, I longed for him to experience this. Also, several of the nursery nurses impressed me greatly. They seemed tuned in to the minds of the children, and able to perpetrate a sort of natural, easy-going interaction which formed a stark contrast to our silent world. I wanted these things for Sam. I felt that these people could help my son in a way that I knew I could not.

4

LOOKING FOR REASONS

By the latter half of his second year, worrying about Sam had become a full-time activity, and it was not only his slow development that concerned me. He had behaviour problems as well, or at least I had problems in dealing with his strange behaviour. The bus journey to our local village became a nightmare. Sam would wriggle incessantly and pull my hair, and although I went through the motions of admonishing him, my protestations were pointless as he did not respond to anything I said. I imagined the looks from other passengers, disapproving and judgemental, every eye upon us. Perhaps they did stare, but I was certainly overly sensitive. Sam rarely looked at anyone, and when he did it was with a sort of darting, sidelong glance. He did not appear to understand what was said to him, and for many years Peter and I assumed that he was not able to do so.

Each morning we awoke to the sound of Sam's inconsolable sobbing. I did not know why he cried and I was not really aware that it was unusual. After half an hour or so he would quieten down. Peter would be off to work as quickly as possible, then I would be alone with my strange, incomprehensible child. He could not be left by himself for a minute without collapsing into despair, and would become upset and obsessive if I tried to do any absorbing activity like reading. So apart from walking, which we did endlessly (I must have pushed that buggy for hundreds of miles), and my singing which he sometimes liked, we had little to fill our days. This was a bad time. Things felt so wrong. We were utterly miserable, and I could see no light ahead.

Sam's state alternated between absent torpor, which depressed me, and frenzied hyperactivity, which made me feel desperate. These bouts of hyperactivity became increasingly frequent. He was now at last mobile, which meant even more difficult to control. He would be up at the sink turning on the taps, throwing things off the table, out of the window, tipping the chairs over, driving me crazy. Sometimes I would literally run after him for several hours until he exhausted himself, and sank once again into his well of aloneness, showing nothing, doing nothing, unreachable.

One day I cracked. I rang the psychologist at the hospital and said I needed help. Now. And then I rang my sister and cried for an hour on the telephone. Within a few weeks it was arranged that Sam should spend one morning each week with a registered childminder at her house. She was wonderful. She collected Sam and took him away for several hours, leaving me with some time for myself. As soon as Sam left I would fling myself into wild physical activity – building garden walls, moving trees, planting hedges – a much needed outlet for my pent-up energy. I landscaped, constructed and planted our garden during these free mornings of mine, and my state of mind improved greatly as a result.

Sam's periods of hyperactivity were as incomprehensible to me as were most other aspects of his behaviour. In fact I had never actually heard the word 'hyperactivity' until one morning when I received a letter from a friend enclosing a newspaper cutting on the subject which described the symptoms in detail.

'I thought that this sounded just like Sam,' said my friend.

And it did. The behaviour of the children who were discussed in the article certainly sounded familiar to me: 'unpredictable and disruptive . . . easily excited and cry often', 'I used to feel a failure because he just would not do as he was told, especially in company. He just used to ignore me'.

This described Sam all right. He displayed many of the symptoms noted as being typical of these hyperactive children. He certainly had the learning disabilities, and looking back over the past two years I could see that he had also shown many signs of allergy common to many of the children. (He had regurgitated food far more than is normal during his first nine months – often up to ten times per day – and our GP had never been able to discover the cause for this. Sam also used to become hot and flushed at times for no apparent reason, and sometimes developed a rash on his cheeks and upper arms. He had an almost continual snuffle, and was prey to stomach upsets and general infections.)

I dared to hope again. Perhaps my son was simply hyperactive. Perhaps we could trace all his disturbances to a physical cause which we could isolate, and then all would be well. I certainly tried. We embarked upon a course that necessitated carefully monitoring Sam's diet. Certain food families were eliminated for a length of time and the results recorded. I noted everything that he ate and drank – the time, the amount, and how he seemed afterwards – in an attempt to interpret his behaviour in terms of what he consumed.

It seems like madness to me now. Sam did suffer from food allergies, but I now believe that while these did produce obvious physical symptoms, his other problems had far more complex causes. However, it took me several years to reach this conclusion, I wanted so much to be on the right track. But eventually I lost my faith in the diet as a cure-all. Although even now I know people who adhere rigidly to a particular diet and believe that a slip can cause immediate behaviour problems, I feel it is stretching credibility too far to say that an individual substance can cause a specific behaviour. But I do think that there is a link between emotional disturbance and allergic reaction, as many of the artificially produced chemicals we consume are not easy to digest, and in expecting our bodies to cope with such substances we are subjecting them to stress. If a person is already suffering from emotional stress – as in the case of a disturbed child – then perhaps the extra demands imposed by an indigestible food tip the body into reacting adversely. So if food allergy is a manifestation of stress overload then it would be more likely to occur in those who are being overstretched emotionally, but it would not actually be the cause of their disturbance. By removing the allergen the stress would be lessened, but the original problem would not be cured.

We joined the Hyperactive Children's Support Group, and although it did not provide the solution to our problems I was glad to have come across the people that we met through them. As a result of this connection Peter and I went to some interesting talks, and I learned to read food labels and to eliminate some of the junk from our diets.

The next step in our search for a physical solution to Sam's problems led us to mega-vitamin therapy. We made contact with a doctor practising in the Home Counties who had adopted an approach used by some American practitioners – that of treating children with learning disabilities and/or autistic problems with massive doses of particular minerals and vitamins. We made the pilgrimage to the south of England, filled yet again with hope, and landed rather the worse for wear in Dr Evans's delightful consulting room in a small town in Sussex.

He was a nice man, interesting and eccentric, and very understanding. When Sam screamed continuously and Peter locked himself in the lavatory, Dr Evans did not bat an eyelid. Even when I was unable to remember our address he seemed unperturbed, and covered my confusion with a story about how he used his ophthalmoscope for reading in the dark when his wife was in bed asleep.

He gave us good advice on how to avoid stress in our lives and explained some of the basics of child-rearing – like how important it is for a child to have a reasonably regular routine for feeding and bathing. The fact that I was ignorant of things as commonsensical as these emerged when Dr Evans's questions revealed that Sam had not had a meal for more than six hours, which could well have accounted for his screaming. In the upheaval of our visit to the south I had forgotten to feed him.

Dr Evans obviously saw that Sam was not the only member of our family who needed help. His perception of our problem was that Peter, Sam and I were probably all suffering from a mineral/vitamin deficiency, which was adversely affecting our behaviour. He arranged for us to send hair samples to an American laboratory for analysis. The results of the tests revealed that we were all carrying an overload of heavy metals in our bodies, and that we were lacking in various minerals and trace elements. We needed large doses of vitamins and minerals to right the balance, it seemed. Dr Evans gave us the feeling that although our lives were presently a jumble of worry and confusion he was going to be able to help us to sort things out with the aid of mega-vitamins.

I applied myself religiously to the new regime of measuring out the powders into little packets, dividing, sorting, listing and charting. At least it created the illusion for me that I was in control.

Sam seemed to start looking better, and Peter was happier and more relaxed, although this may have been because I was now devoting as much time to him and his vitamins and tablets as I was to Sam's needs.

We visited Dr Evans only two or three times but he wrote to us and we spoke on the telephone occasionally. The support that we got from these letters and the feeling of being in touch with someone who cared about our problems was helpful, but with a five-hundred-mile round trip for each consultation, not to mention the expense of the mega-vitamin therapy itself, we felt that this kind of help was costing us too much.

The help on offer locally was of a different kind. We were still under the auspices of the child development unit, and Sam's psychologist, Don, decided to try Sam with a teaching scheme called Portage. Once a week Don came to visit us at home in order to demonstrate a simple procedure that I was to follow through with Sam. The idea was that he should be asked to do a task five times each day and the results plotted on a graph; it was presumably hoped that eventually the graph would reveal an increase in the number of times Sam had complied with my request. A more pointless exercise I could not imagine. Why on earth should Sam touch his nose five times, even supposing that he had wanted to oblige me, which he most certainly did not? Sam may or may not have understood what was being said to him during these sessions, but he had no more desire to reciprocate overtures made by another person than he had to communicate for his own sake.

Despite not being interested in the job in hand, Sam enjoyed Don's visits. He was particularly interested in Don's beard, and would always rush to fetch his bib – a rigid plastic object – whenever Don appeared. Sam would sit happily clutching his bib and glancing from it to the beard and back again, in obvious appreciation of the similarity between the two.

He took great pleasure in similarities like this and they seemed to hold much significance for him. Sometimes when the cat vacated her position on the sofa he would rush to find his toy monkey, a tiny object of about two inches long, and place it carefully where she had been, smiling as he did so. He had many soft toys that to me seemed more appropriate cat substitutes, but to him it was the tail that was all-important. He would touch the monkey's tail, ever so gently, and dart a fleeting glance at the cat. One day he noticed a wet patch on the kitchen floor. He stopped dead and then ran in great excitement to the room next door to a spot where he had peed on the carpet the day before. Sam felt the carpet and compared, and when wetness matched wetness, his face broke into a smile of pure joy.

He was also becoming more interested in his toys, several of which were musical. He liked to set them all playing at once, tinkling away simultaneously, and would engage in a frenzied winding as soon as one dared to stop. It seemed that none of the toys was allowed to cease playing whilst the others continued, thereby making it impossible to break the cycle. Sam would get very upset about his inability to solve this problem, and often had to be removed from the room until his musical toys had wound themselves down.

Just when I was beginning to feel that there would never be any sort of communication between Sam and myself, he made a breakthrough. Although small in itself, the event seemed momentous to me. Sam pointed. He was two years old. It was more like a vague motion with his hand, but there was no mistaking the fact that he was indicating something to me. This was communication, even if only by gesture. It was as though a thin line had been drawn between us, linking us, but flimsy and vulnerable like the merest thread of cobweb.

In an optimistic mood I wrote in my diary:

Now I am very much happier with Sam and sometimes feel that he is wonderful, although of course I am still very worried about his development. We have no idea how he will turn out or why he is slow with things and so uncommunicative. In fact he now seems to have caught up a great deal but is still not saying any words. He seems to understand between about fifty and one hundred, although it is difficult to be sure. He will point, sort of, and will occasionally fetch things when asked to do so.

Unfortunately my happier frame of mind was short-lived. Several months previously we had sought a second opinion regarding our son's condition from the child guidance training centre at High

Wick Hospital. The report now arrived, and Sam's psychologist revealed its depressing contents to us. Although Sam may have had an autistic phase, it stated, this was no longer present. He was retarded on a general level, with an IQ of fifty. I found this devastating, and also hard to believe. Just two weeks before, Peter's parents had been staying and had chastised us for imagining that there was anything at all wrong with our son. 'He's perfectly normal,' they said. 'You're just being neurotic. Stop worrying.'

I began to feel quite lost in the maze of uncertainty and became determined to find someone who could tell me something about my son and what to expect for his future. I wanted a definitive diagnosis. A book called *Toys and Playthings*, by Elizabeth Newson, set me off in the right direction. This woman seemed to know all about non-communicating children, so I telephoned her. She was connected with the child development unit at Nottingham University, one of the main diagnostic centres for autism in this country. Having ploughed through the red tape of medical ethics and referrals we eventually went to meet her at Nottingham University – Peter, Sam, myself and the potty, for it came everywhere with us these days. We ate our sandwiches and then walked in the park until the time of our appointment. From the time that we entered the diagnostic clinic I had the feeling we were in the hands of people who knew exactly what they were doing.

Peter and I sat with Dr Newson, who talked with us and took notes while observing Sam together with a play therapist through a one-way-mirror wall. Dr Newson said that while a definite prognosis was not possible she did think that Sam was autistic, and in her opinion would go on to develop the full-blown syndrome. A complete report would be sent to us, she promised, stating the details of the various observational sessions and her opinions regarding our son. Several months later it arrived:

Observational session
Mary, working with Sam in the playroom, describes the 'feel' of the session as follows:

During the session, Sam engaged in activities mainly of his own choosing, rarely showing any spontaneous interest in what I presented to him. For much of the time he was absorbed in his own fascination with wheels or peas; getting through to him either by joining in these activities or by inveigling him away was extremely hard work. Even then I felt I was only obtaining his *attention*, not his interest.

No relationship developed between us, yet I formed a strong respect and liking for Sam. He remained indifferent to my presence most of the time without seeking to put distance between us. Indeed I was struck by his tolerance for discomfort, for the unfamiliar and for my pressurizing him, all the more surprising as he was clearly suffering from a cold. When I tried to get Sam started on a new activity it was necessary to hold him firmly. Invariably he struggled to get away, determined to return to his own occupation rather than because he disliked being held. When he knocked himself twice, Sam seemed not to register this in his anxiety to resume his turning of the wheels. Or perhaps because he had hurt himself he turned to the wheels for solace. Sam engaged in very little direct eye-contact, nor did he make use of sideways glances or the mirror to see what I was doing. His attention was object-oriented. If my gestures, indicating an action (e.g., pressing the bar to open the till) were closely allied to the object, he appeared to take notice of the gesture and would then carry out the movement. When gesture and object were separated by time or space, Sam was clearly less able to comprehend the non-verbal signal.

Sam's verbal comprehension was restricted to simple instructions, yet I suspected that often 'getting through to him' was the difficulty first and foremost rather than making myself understood. At no point did I detect mutation of words or intonation in Sam's utterances nor any spontaneous meaningful sounds.

It was difficult to assess Sam's cognitive competence. Often he seemed unaware of the purpose of an activity, such as placing the pegs into round holes, or the floor formboards. I had to cue him repeatedly on to each new stage of a puzzle as well as prevent him from removing the pieces once in position. The object of the exercise eluded him, and my praises for his efforts seemed to fall upon deaf ears. In other ways Sam showed clearly his ability to think his way through a problem. In the reception area he ushered me into position then motioned me to pick him up (by lifting his arms) so he could reach the hanging parrot. He explored everything thoroughly, would come away if requested, then found his own way back to whatever he had been attracted to without difficulty.

My overriding impression of playing with Sam was that, to keep his attention and to distract him from his preoccupation, I was handicapped by having only two arms and one pair of eyes. Ideally I could have used six of each for holding him, focusing his attention, shaping up the actions, watching his face for signs of response, comprehension etc. Certainly I felt there were more sparks in Sam than I was able to fan effectively in this session.

The report concluded:

Sam is still very young for a diagnosis to be made. None the less, he does present as a rather classically autistic child, and there seems rather little room for doubt that the diagnosis of autism will be confirmed over the next year or two of his development.

Sam clearly conformed to the main points considered to be essential for a diagnosis of autism to be made, these being:

1) Language impairment, including all modes of communication
2) Social impairment, including poor eye contact
3) Evidence of rigidity of thought patterns, including ritualistic and obsessional behaviour
4) Onset of the above three elements before the age of two and a half years.

So now we knew for certain. Sam was autistic. The morning that I received the report I wandered through the woods, sweet-smelling and damp after rain. I collapsed under a clump of birches at the end of our ridge. My thoughts were a jumble of petty fears and real terror. I was now part of a minority group – parents of handicapped children – people who seemed so irrelevant to real life, to important things. I could never show off my child – he would never complement me in any way. He would need so much extra – more money, more time, more emotional resources. I could not give him these things. I had nothing to give. I was afraid of making demands upon people and felt I could not possibly cope with the burden of a handicapped child.

My memory of sitting on the bus with Sam came flooding back. His strange behaviour, people looking at me, staring, judging, criticizing. 'Please let me die,' I thought, 'and let him die too.'

I lay there staring up into the trees for hours, watching the bits of sky come and go through the rippling leaves. The breeze died. There was silence. I felt stranded, stunned, trapped in eternity. I tried to focus upon the reality of my situation but was unable to do so. Then, like a pattern of shadows appearing suddenly as the sun emerges from behind a cloud, came the thought, 'If ever I come to understand this child, I will understand myself.'

This idea became the root of the determination that sustained me through the years ahead. I recognized that his and my destiny were inextricably bound together and that only by confronting his problems might I eventually hope to unravel some of my own.

Perhaps it is only when the fabric of day-to-day life is torn to the extent that things cannot go on as before that people really begin to confront their deep-seated emotional problems. Peeling back the layers from a successfully concealed wound can seem pointless so long as life offers compensations for lack of self-awareness. And yet it is only by doing this that real healing can occur, bringing with it the opportunity to take control of one's life.

Sam and his problems were certainly forcing me to confront aspects of myself that I would have preferred not to see. I sank into depression – probably to avoid thinking about anything at all – and stayed there for many months. Eventually I pulled myself out of it by taking action. Sam had by this time started going to the council nursery – where I knew that he would be safe for a time – but we had to consider the possibility that he might need special schooling. The Autistic Society sent me literature about their own specially run schools, of which there were eight spread around the country. Because Peter worked for a television company, and as jobs were not impossible to come by in those days, it seemed conceivable that he might be able to move to another station. We studied the map of England and Wales – making red dots for television stations, blue dots for

Autistic Society schools – and pinpointed three places where a television station and a school were within reasonable distance of one another. These were Plymouth, Southampton and Maidstone. I made arrangements to see the schools and off we went. First stop Plymouth, which I personally favoured.

The school, like our house, was delightfully situated, in a wooded area some distance from the nearest village. The children, we were told, had contact with children from an ordinary school nearby, and had good facilities for riding and other sporting activities. It sounded attractive, but I gained no understanding of any of the children that we saw, of how they functioned, or of what the staff were trying to do with them. Some seemed to be extremely intelligent – working at computers and other apparatus – some very retarded, and all unbelievably strange. None of them looked at us – a race of aliens. We left, mystified.

The school at Southampton we could not visit for some reason, so it was onwards to Gravesend. Here we three spent the morning amongst a nursery group with whom we then had lunch. I was impressed by the way that these young and mostly very withdrawn children were able actually to do things, such as lay the table and use a knife and fork, when so far as I could see there was no way of reaching them in order to teach these skills.

Affecting the behaviour of somebody who for whatever reason does not interact in the normal way is difficult. Quite apart from the frustration that results from talking to a person who does not respond, there is the problem of maintaining sufficient confidence to continue speaking when there is no feedback. It is necessary to adopt a blind belief that the person hears you, and understands you, and that what you are saying is actually relevant to them. But the children that we were with had learned how to do things, and so I felt that Sam could too. Exactly how, I had no idea.

We looked over the school and spoke briefly with some of the older children. Watching them in the playground from an upstairs window highlighted the peculiarity of the way in which these children behaved. They were rigid and obsessional, both in speech (when they did speak) and in their actions. The games in progress below obviously had rules that were slavishly adhered to. One boy was throwing a ball against a wall, catching it, then following an exact routine of clapping, running round the playground, touching various objects, and then returning to his original position to begin the whole procedure again. Why should people do such things, I wondered.

We set off for home with much food for thought. If we decided to move nearer to one of the Autistic Society schools, then we would obviously have to sell our home. I felt ambivalent about the idea. Now that the house was beginning to take shape I did not really want to leave it. Peter was uncertain too, and there was always the chance that he might not be able to get a job in the area where we wanted to be. Neither was there any guarantee that the local education authority would finance a place for Sam at an Autistic Society school, even though both schools had said that they would be willing to accept him as a pupil. There seemed to be so much uncertainty attached to the idea of relocating our lives – perhaps it was simply more than we could cope with. But for whatever reason, the idea of moving south gradually began to fade, and we confined ourselves to seeking help for our son in the place where we were already living.

5

NURSERY

Before he started school Sam went to the day nursery for seven months or so. One of the greatest gains during this period, as far as I was concerned at least, was that he became toilet trained. The prospect of persuading him to give up nappies had seemed daunting, yet there he was, taking his place alongside the other children sitting in a row on the nursery's miniature toilets. How sweet he looked. I was so pleased. It was one thing that I no longer had to worry about.

For the three mornings each week Sam went to the nursery Peter would drop him off on his way to work. Sam hardly seemed aware of me as I fastened him into his car seat – sometimes looking absent, sometimes tense and anxious, but always clutching his small plastic aeroplane. He held that aeroplane so tightly, as if his very life depended upon it. We had no idea when we gave it to him of the importance that it would assume, nor that his fascination with aircraft would continue for many years.

From the time when Sam had first noticed that there were things going on above him he would gaze into the sky, entranced by the noisy, flying beasts that must have appeared to come and go as if by magic. He was completely enraptured when he was actually given one. From that time Sam's sense of involvement with the planes and helicopters that buzzed overhead seemed to increase. He would stand in the garden, peering upwards but occasionally stealing a reassuring glance at the aeroplane that he held clenched in his hand. Perhaps the flying objects represented power and freedom to Sam. Perhaps he envied them their ability to just fly away – he must surely have wanted to do the same thing himself at times.

But what Sam did think or feel I could only guess at, for he was not able to ask questions about the things that went on around him. I do not think that he even formulated such ideas at this time of his life, for I doubt whether he was enough in touch with the real world to query its workings. What he perceived he either ignored or fitted immediately into the rigid framework of understanding within which he functioned.

At nursery school Sam was in the group with the oldest and most experienced of the nursery nurses. He appeared to become very fond of her. She was affectionate and understanding, and could probably have helped Sam a great deal more than she did had she not been so overworked. Even so, she did manage to persuade him to sit at table and eat his meals with the rest of the group. He learned to tolerate the other children, even if he did not acknowledge or communicate with them, and although mixing with his peers did not make Sam any more sociable, it helped him to become more socialized. But the time came when we accepted that Sam would have to leave this now familiar environment. It was becoming overcrowded and the staff felt that they could no longer give him the support that he needed.

We had visited a school which had been suggested by the psychologist at the child development unit, where there was a nursery unit for children with special needs. Theoretically the children who attended the unit should be there for a limited period of time only (we were told for up to a year) while their educational requirements were being assessed. Then they were either accepted by the school as full-time pupils, or sent on to schools considered to be appropriate to their needs. Compared with the day nursery this school unit seemed well endowed. Sam would be in a group of six children, with a teacher and an assistant, in a bright cheerful room where there was lots of teaching equipment. The only stumbling block was that in order for our son to attend this school we would have to sign a form stating our belief that he required special education. I still found this a painful admission, and so did Peter. We both wanted to hold on to the idea that Sam could manage in a normal environment for as long as possible, and I felt also that being with ordinary children in our local playgroup might help moderate our son's behaviour. Peter and I rarely had any real discussion about Sam's problems, which may be why I often wrote down my thoughts on the subject:

> I was impressed by what the school staff told us regarding their aims and methods and was pleased that they seemed to like Sam so much. They actually appeared to want him to go there, which was lovely. I would feel fairly secure about him being in such a place, and that he was in good hands and getting the sort of help he needs. They might be able to pinpoint his areas of difficulty more accurately than anybody else has been able to do. I just can't decide whether Sam should go there or to an ordinary playschool. I feel that he might be better off at playschool – where at least he would be with normal children – providing the person in charge was able to persuade him to join in with the other children and so help him to catch up with them. If he was not able to do this, however, he would be losing valuable time in a situation that was of little benefit to him.

The nearer we got to the time when we would have to make a decision regarding Sam's future, the more obvious it was becoming that he needed all the help that he could get. He was developing some alarming habits, such as a continual exaggerated swallowing and a sort of low growl. The gap between Sam and his peers was widening. He had also become firmly entrenched in the habit – common among autistic children – of always carrying a hard object clenched in his hand. He no longer insisted on this being his aeroplane, it could be almost anything – a carrot, his beaker, a stick, a toy car – but it had to *be* there. Sam was now becoming wrapped in his cloak of autism. We opted for the special school. I summed up Sam's nursery days in my diary:

> Today is Sam's last day at the nursery and I am sad that he is leaving there. I think that he has enjoyed going – at least he has seemed happy when Peter called to collect him – and I have felt relieved that he was with normal children. He will miss Terry who has looked after him – she is such a kind and gentle person. He seems to like her – he often looks at her photograph. I love to think of him having somebody else in his life to whom he is

attached – it takes the edge off my worry about the fact that he is so alone.

Being at the nursery has helped Sam considerably, although I must not forget that he was often left to his own devices which was not really good for him. Even so it was a good environment for him to be in. There were plenty of things going on all the time, which meant that there was always something for Sam to latch on to if he felt like doing so. For example he often wandered into the kitchen where the kitchen ladies chatted to him or let him 'help' with the cleaning. Also the children would talk to him, and even though he didn't respond, it was setting up some sort of communication of which he was certainly aware.

Another benefit has been that during the past month there has been a great improvement in Sam's eating habits. He has begun to chew his food at last and will occasionally pick up pieces of apple or bread. He will now eat rice and 'green bits', which he used to spit out. About six weeks ago he started drinking from a cup while he was actually at the nursery. Terry sent the cup home with him, but he refuses to use it here and will only use a spouted cup. I hope that now he is leaving the nursery this short spell of drinking from a proper cup will not prove to be another dead end. It's important that he learn how to do this because he now looks too old to be using a spouted cup. I'm sure that the improvements that have occurred in Sam's eating and drinking habits during the past six months are due to his being at the nursery. I don't know whether Terry has actually taught him to do the things that he has learned or whether he has simply imitated the other children.

In some ways this period of our lives was one of our happier times as a family. I had some time to pursue my own interests, and Peter had the stimulation and interest of his job. He was doing well at work and had begun to make some friends there. We started having people over for dinner and our social life improved. The underlying worry about Sam still existed, but sometimes I managed to forget about it. In any case, he seemed to be easier to cope with at this time, despite the fact that he was developing some very peculiar habits: he insisted that all our kitchen chairs should lie on their sides instead of standing upright and that the arm-rest covers on our sofa be turned and folded in a particular way. Sam would check periodically to see that nobody had undone his handiwork in arranging these objects just so. But his hyperactivity had subsided and he was sleeping better. The three of us also did more of what I considered to be 'proper family things', such as outings and visits together. These filled me with a deep sense of satisfaction that to some extent masked the unhappy times in between.

A glance through our photograph album would have revealed nothing but the happy family of which I so longed to be a part, yet in putting together the album I was very selective. I created a harmonious picture of our lives which did not represent the true state of our affairs. It was as though there were two quite separate realities. At the time I used to think that it was like living in a world of dreams where the people and settings – the most obvious reality – served only as props for the ongoing emotional drama that was taking place. Most of what Peter and I said to each other bore little relation to what we felt on a deeper level. Sometimes for quite long periods of time we went through the motions of family life but for us the real action was being played out on a different stage altogether.

Neither of us had had much stability during our formative years and we were both insecure. Now we each felt controlled by the other and we each in turn manipulated the other to our own ends. We both got hurt in the process. I remember often feeling that Peter was angry with me – it was as though I had committed some terrible, unnamed crime. Many years later I realized what that crime was.

By having a baby I had unwittingly re-created for Peter the painful situation that he had experienced as a young child; a situation where he felt himself to be excluded from his mother's affections by the arrival of a new baby. The early part of his life had been unsettled and difficult. When at two years of age he was uprooted, moved to a different country, presented with a stepfather, and then within a short space of time expected to share his mother with a new-born baby, he must have felt panic-stricken. Peter's stepsister had problems which demanded a great deal of her mother's time and Peter was probably lonely and frightened – angry at his mother for failing to give him the support that he needed and resentful towards the baby for taking his mother away so often. Perhaps Sam's birth unleashed these long-buried emotions. But from my point of view, Peter's anger and intermittent rejection of Sam and myself seemed inexcusable. I resented his actions bitterly, but nevertheless felt that I must be blameworthy because he was so awful to me.

It seemed impossible to disentangle the matted strands of my relationship with Peter. But looking back upon those days from a more distant perspective I can discern patterns in our behaviour. It seems to me that when Peter treated Sam badly he felt guilty for doing so and he then blamed me for the misery that he suffered as a consequence. This made me furious, but I was afraid of showing my feelings. Perhaps I unconsciously offloaded my anger on to Sam. I also felt guilty about my ambivalent feelings towards Sam, and about keeping him in a destructive situation I knew should end.

This was our real world, tacitly agreed though neither admitted nor comprehended by either of us. And yet in some ways Peter and I understood each other very well. We spoke to each other in a symbolic sort of language, cryptic to the degree that a friend told me that she often had no idea what we were talking about. No wonder that our son had communcation difficulties.

Because Sam was less agitated and easier to handle than he had been, I dared to think that he might be 'getting better'. I realized much later how terribly unhappy he must have felt. During this period he was often ill with fevers that seemed to come from nowhere and overwhelm him for days on end. Scarcely a month went by without his having a course of antibiotic treatment, which appeared to do no good at all. Sometimes he clutched at his head as though in pain – I remember fearing that he was about to have a fit. At other times he would cover his eyes, or his ears, as though hypersensitive to his environment. On these occasions the merest glimpse of his surroundings or the slightest sound seemed to cause Sam excruciating pain.

Sam's first day at his new school – the special school that we had been to see – came and went without incident. For several months he went for three days each week, journeying to and fro in the taxi provided by the education authority. I worried about his unavoidably long journey of almost an hour each way, for it meant that a large proportion of his day was spent in a car. As Sam had no language, his teacher kept me in touch with his school activities through a notebook which came home with him every few days. This worked reasonably well as a means of communication between Mrs Stanley and myself, although its use was really limited to passing on factual information. It did not fill the void of ignorance I felt regarding what Sam actually did for the seven hours that he was away – how he behaved, how he felt. The little boy who arrived home at 3.45 p.m. conveyed nothing to me, and I understood little of what he experienced. I would carry him from the taxi initially happy to see him, but soon feeling rejected and distanced from him. Then we would go for one of our inevitable walks, rain or shine, after which we would sit and wait for Peter to come home. During these walks life seemed to assume a sort of timeless quality. The hours, days and weeks stretched endlessly before us. Nothing ever seemed to change, apart from the seasons. In winter I would bump Sam's pushchair over the frozen rutted tracks. By March the lambs would have appeared in the fields. They did not interest Sam, but we would stop to look at them anyway. Then as the weather grew warmer in April and May I would park the pushchair and carry Sam up to the top of a ridge from which we could sometimes see for twenty miles. In summer we wandered across the hillsides while I searched for wild flowers, or through the fields Sam loved because of the huge harvesting machines which impressed him enormously.

Some mornings I would visit Sam's school. At the time I described his teacher, Mrs Stanley, as 'calm and patient, probably good at her job but not particularly loving'. Sam appeared to like her and I think he appreciated the more structured environment of the schoolroom after the somewhat chaotic experience of the day nursery.

Predictability is all important to autistic children; rigidity of thinking is one of the diagnostic criteria of the condition. This can manifest itself in a variety of ways. One of the most common is an insistence by the child that a precise route is followed each time a particular journey is undertaken. Fortunately Sam was not like this, but I have know children who screamed incessantly if their mothers deviated by more than a few yards from their normal route.

Sam showed the same sort of obsessional behaviour in other ways. Only weeks after starting school he developed a habit that has stayed with him ever since, although it has altered in form. He would pull a handful of grass, then rub it gently between the fingers of his raised hand as he allowed it to flutter gradually to the ground. His eyes remained fixated upon the grass, and as it was only a few inches from his face the procedure had a mesmerizing effect. Whatever might be happening around him was completely excluded as he became locked into his own self-limiting activity. It drove me almost frantic to see Sam indulging in this grass-picking obsession. For one thing it made him look so strange, and totally unreachable. But it made me aware of certain 'cutting-off' habits of my own, causing me to re-experience the dreadful sense of alienation that results from the blocking off of one's emotions.

If Sam was interrupted or prevented from continuing with his grass-picking, he became very upset. It is probable that many of the occasions when he became agitated for no apparent reason were caused by his failure to manipulate his environment in the exact way he wanted.

This insistence upon sameness is a determination to have absolute control over a tiny part of one's life. Autistic children feel vulnerable, for they do not have a properly developed sense of their own identities. They have no belief in their ability to affect their surroundings, or in their own potential. Because they live in constant fear of being attacked or overwhelmed they adopt a rigid stance in order to defend themselves against the unknown. But this crude method of dealing with the world creates an all-or-nothing situation. By his rejecting manner the child usually manages to deter those who attempt to communicate with him. But if he does not do so then he had no protection other than his autistic withdrawal. He has no weapons, and no tools with which to negotiate. Nor is he able to acquire the more subtle forms of behaviour because his isolation ensures that the strict patterns of existence remain unmodified.

According to Mrs Stanley, Sam settled in reasonably well at school, except that he clung to her and got upset when expected to change from one activity to another. One thing that did worry me was his refusal to drink while he was there. I did not know why this was, but I suspected that it might be the old drinking-cup problem re-emerging. I explained to Mrs Stanley via the notebook:

Sam is drinking properly at home so I don't know what the problem is. But he is extremely sensitive about the whole area of drinking and anything to do with his cup, which was for a time one of his 'carrying objects'. Are you giving him an ordinary cup, rather than the one with the spout? A few months ago I tried to wean him off the spouted cup and he became so deeply worried that both his eating and drinking habits were very disturbed for some time. He used to lift the food or drink to his mouth, but could not seem to get it inside. It seemed to be stuck somehow. He would hold the spoon or cup against his lips, and then get very upset. I was worried because he started losing weight, and so put the spout back on to his cup again. Gradually he got over this trauma and resumed normal eating and drinking, but I have never again had the courage to try persuading him to relinquish his spout. I know that he should not still be drinking from this sort of cup at his age but perhaps it would be best to leave him be for the present.

Now I see that Sam was clinging to the old way of doing things – sucking like a baby instead of drinking like an older child – because he was overloaded by the changes in his life. The whole business of leaving the nursery (and the one other person in his life with whom he had formed any sort of bond) and starting school must have been terribly worrying for him. He was after all only three years old, disturbed and emotionally immature. But he seemed calm, and so I thought that he was coping. Little did I understand that starting school was the start of a sequence of events which would prove to be very difficult for Sam. I had decided that he should have his bedroom decorated, as he had lived with 1950s yellow and blue chrysanthemums for long enough, but it never occurred to me that together with the new school this might not be a good time to create more upheaval and change in his life. I was angry when he started tearing off the new wallpaper that I had so painstakingly hung, but still failed to get his message. Then Sam began climbing out of his cot. We removed it, and replaced it with a bed. New school, new room colour, new bed. It must have seemed to Sam as though his whole world was being torn apart. And so began his serious sleep problems. Sam refused to stay in his room alone. When left there at bedtime he would weep and bang on his door until he eventually fell to the floor exhausted. This would wake him up, he would start to cry again, and so it would go on all night. Peter and I soon gave up on trying to persuade Sam to go to sleep on his own. We would take turns by his bed, holding his hand until he dropped off. This often took many hours, and as Sam could not tolerate having the light on it meant sitting in the dark, waiting, for what used to seem an eternity. As the stress upon Peter and me mounted, the cracks in our relationship began to show. We argued constantly. Sam started wetting his pants. We were desperate for some sort of escape and so decided to take a short trip, unbelievably stupidly it now seems to me, for this was the last thing that Sam needed to help him settle.

A month later we took another trip – this time to visit my sister in the south of England. By now Sam was very withdrawn indeed. It was almost as though he had given up rebelling and instead had retreated further and further into himself and into his autism. We had been staying with my sister for two days with Sam being isolated by day, screaming at night, when suddenly his behaviour altered. I was amazed, and wrote in my diary:

> Sam has been detached and unreachable all morning, and making dreadful throaty noises. Suddenly in the pub he started making overtures towards Alice [my niece]. It was marvellous to watch. He smiled and touched her gently, and became very coy. Then he insisted that she put her hand on my arm – he likes the people he cares about to be sort of linked together. He has never met her before but really seems to adore her – it is such a shame that he probably will not see her again for a very long time.

Sam's behaviour on this occasion, and on several similar ones, resembled nothing so much as flirting. It seemed extraordinary that a child who was apparently so unaware of the ways in which people communicate with each other, should indulge in such sophisticated behaviour. The placing of Alice's hand on my arm by Sam was similar to his joining together of people's hands, which he did on and off for about a year. I think that it started as a bringing together of those who mattered – perhaps he felt that welded together they might form a more solid base of support for him than they could manage as individuals. But I think that the purpose of his linking altered. One of my most painful memories is of Peter and me shouting angrily at each other across a room and Sam running pathetically between the two of us, pulling each of our hands, trying to mend the break and join us back together again. It is a measure of how disturbed we were ourselves that we could be so cruel as to ignore his plea. He eventually stopped trying to mend the break at about the time he stopped rebelling generally. He just gave up.

Sam's development was noticeably retarded by this time and although I had no idea of what was happening to him, or indeed to any of us, instinctively I felt his problems were related to Peter's and mine. Yet none of the doctors, psychologists or teachers that we came across shared this view. I could not understand why. On one hand it was perfectly apparent that Sam's general development and communication skills were well behind those of his peers. On the other it was equally clear that he was very insecure – he could not bear to be left alone and he had severe sleeping problems.

Retarded development and emotional disturbances are always detectable at some stage in autistic children, which to me made it worth considering that the two might be related in some way, or even that one might be contingent upon the other. As the child grows older his behaviour becomes more complex and more difficult to interpret, and the picture becomes clouded. But I believe that in the early years of a child's life the links between emotional disturbance and delayed development are clearly visible for those who wish to see them.

I had only just begun to wonder about such things when quite by chance I came across an advertisement in a video magazine for a machine that was being used in a special unit for studying and treating autistic children. I contacted the woman who ran this unit and she came to see Sam with a view to possibly accepting him into her small group of half a dozen or so children. In the unit, the behaviour of each child was carefully monitored by recording it on videotape. As I understood it, the aim was to discover a link between cause and effect. Although Sam did not get a place in the unit I was glad to have come across it, for only after doing so did I become aware of the more intricate aspects of human behaviour.

I was particularly interested as I had recently read about the work done by a doctor who videotaped the responses of new-born infants to the different expressions that appeared on their mothers' faces. The results were striking. The babies showed the most distress not when shown an angry face, as might be expected, but when shown an apathetic face with an absence of expression such as would be worn by somebody who was depressed. If people were able to record and make sense of the minutiae of human interaction, I thought, then it must be possible to understand in a broader sense the ways in which we relate to each other, and how it can go wrong. I knew nothing about psychology at this time and my ideas concerning these things were vague to say the least, but looking at Sam's lack of development as a consequence of his withdrawal from world certainly made sense to me.

6

HOLDING THERAPY

When Jennifer Stonecross walked in through the door I was waiting. Like a sponge, I was ready to absorb whatever she had to tell me. Jennifer was a holding therapist. She had been booked by the local branch of the Autistic Society to give a talk about her ideas and methods of treatment. The branch secretary, Lisa, knew that I believed there was an emotional aspect to autism and telephoned me before the talk thinking I might like to meet Jennifer personally. I was delighted. Jennifer had precisely the sort of ideas that I wanted to explore.

She believed that autism was some sort of emotional disturbance, and that while parents should not feel guilty, environment did play a big part in its development. Jennifer appeared to understand my concern about the way that Sam and I had always seemed so distanced from each other and was convinced that holding therapy would help us. She also believed that autism was curable, and this idea obviously appealed to me. I decided almost immediately that holding therapy was just what we needed.

I invited Jennifer, Lisa and some other parents from the Autistic Society to my house for lunch. By the time we reached the walnut and raisin ice-cream it had become apparent that we divided neatly into two camps – Jennifer and myself, and the others.

Jennifer did not go down well at the Autistic Society. As soon as people realized that she was citing emotional derailment as the cause of the affliction their children suffered, most parents switched off. They could not bear the idea that their children's problems might be in any way associated with parenting or environment. I could understand why.

Such ideas raised all sorts of worrying questions, and were simply too painful to contemplate. Like Peter and me, many of the parents Jennifer spoke to were struggling to cope with the disruptive behaviour of their autistic children. Their belief that they were doing the best job in difficult circumstances might have been all they had to hold on to. This would have been lost if they had allowed themselves to think of their children as emotionally disturbed, for then they would have felt implicated. Perhaps they needed to feel that they were 'good' parents, just in order to survive.

The sheer hard work involved in looking after a handicapped child is itself exhausting. It can be especially disheartening with a condition such as autism, which is unpredictable and apparently arbitrary in its progress. Uncertainty about the future adds to the strain of living with a child whose bizarre and non-responsive reactions cause parents like us to feel rejected and ineffectual. All parents of autistic children have ridden the emotional see-saw of hope and disappointment. Their children look intelligent and sometimes seem to offer great promise of future progress. They can be extremely skilful in isolated areas. A ray of hope can pierce the gloom only to be smothered by despair as progress fails to continue.

Many times I have watched the light of interest kindle in my son's eyes, only to see it doused by apathy. His development would then stagnate for long periods, stifling my hopes for his future. Sometimes I felt life would be easier if I could just accept my fate and live with the fact that I could not alter our situation. But fate does not provide an explanation, and I wanted one – however painful it turned out to be. I needed to know how my family had got into the dire state we were in and why my son was clad in an emotional suit of armour. Jennifer Stonecross seemed to have some of the answers.

She was a qualified psychologist, but had not done specific training as a therapist. The ideas and methods she used in the holding-therapy sessions stemmed from Dr Martha Welch, an American, who evolved and used the therapy in her clinic. Dr Welch believes that autism is emotional damage that can be repaired by holding therapy:

Autism is caused by faulty bonding between mother and child.

The fact that the children cured of autism through mother-child holding therapy show no residual organic pathology suggests that environmental factors, namely aspects of the mother-child interaction, play the largest role in the etiology of autism. Children are born with different sensitivities and vulnerabilities. However, some mothers will not give up on a withdrawn child. Others will conclude that he prefers to be left alone. Still others will neglect a child's needs, albeit unwittingly, until he gives up from frustration and hopelessness.

The benefit of holding therapy accrues equally to the mother and to the child. The mothers seem to lack normal instincts toward their autistic children prior to treatment. They are unable to understand their needs or to respond in any normal fashion.

Dr Welch acted in a supervisory capacity towards Jennifer Stonecross. She helped and advised, mostly by letter or telephone but backed up by occasional visits. Sometimes Jennifer would take a list of questions from me, telephone Dr Welch during the week, then come back later with the answers.

She sent me a copy of a paper written jointly by herself and Dr Welch, in which they describe holding therapy:

Mothers, place your child on your lap face to face with you. Put the child's arms around you under your arms. Be sure to do it in such a way that the child cannot escape. If the child is a teenager, put the child beside you instead of on your lap. Fathers, when possible, hold your wife while she holds your child. Or, you hold the other children while your wife holds one. The other children will wait patiently as long as they know that their turn will come.

The child being held will list dozens of excuses as to why you should let go: 'I'm hungry', 'I won't be your friend' etc. The older the child, the more elaborate and sophisticated the excuses. Mothers, you must hold on no matter how fierce the battle becomes. Your child may insult you or try to hurt you. When the fighting dies down the child often cries more in sorrow than in anger, and then you can comfort him or her. Meanwhile your own feelings of upset and anger towards the child can be safely expressed in this way.

Usually the child uses only a small portion of his strength. If he succeeds in escaping, he will look for you to catch him. Once the child feels certain that the mother will hold on, he relaxes in his mother's arms, and there is a time of play and mutual enjoyment.

Mothers, hold each child daily through the fighting period until the mutually loving period. In addition to a regular holding time, hold your child any time he signals distress such as by a tantrum or other misbehaviour. The frequency of such behaviour will diminish.

Jennifer told me about the mothering centre she ran single-handed. She held a weekly group for mothers to practise holding therapy with their children – along the lines laid down by Dr Welch. The children's problems ranged in their degree of severity from slightly disruptive behaviour to total autistic withdrawal. Jennifer's work at the mothering centre was on a more or less voluntary basis. It was something she believed in. She charged mothers very little to attend a holding-therapy session and probably made next to nothing after paying for hire of the room in the community centre where she held the weekly sessions.

Her main job was that of home tutor to an autistic girl, which was how she had become interested in autism and subsequently holding therapy. Her pupil, Caroline, responded to Jennifer's belief in her intelligence, which she held despite Caroline's odd behaviour and almost total lack of verbal communication. Jennifer encouraged Caroline to communicate in writing, which she learned to do, eventually taking some GCE examinations. When Caroline began to write, she used the medium to describe some of her feelings, her fears, and her longing to be understood. During her talk to the Autistic Society Jennifer showed us some of Caroline's writing:

Caroline wanted to talk so much but it seemed to be an impossible task do you think she will ever talk was the question that everyone always asked her mother and her teacher to which they replied she might one day there is no reason why she shouldn't all the apparatus is there she used to talk when she was a little girl some people found this hard to believe they thought that her parents must be deluding themselves and that she had always been silent but she had spoken she could remember quite clearly the times she had said things to her mummy look at the moon she said one day caught by the sudden beauty of it in the daytime sky she must have been about six years old at the time lost in her misery but still responsive to beauty coming unawares from the heavens. she could remember other times when she had tried to say things but had been caught in the black web of her unhappiness and unable to utter a sound it is very difficult to explain the way in which her fear gripped her vocal chords it felt as though unseen hands were pressing on her throat struggling to extinguish life itself such a little place for the air to come and go and so little room for the mysterious life force to exist that area of her body seemed so especially vulnerable so very exposed that it must be protected at all costs even the cost of silence that seemed to save valuable air for the process of life itself there was none to spare for eventual speech so speech had to go no one realized that this was one of the fears behind the silence this sense of tight breathlessness that seemed to suffocate and threaten what little life there was with extinction. this was a real feeling when she was a tiny girl but it was not until she was nearly grown up that she had the detachment to describe it so it was the same with so many feelings now that she was older she could give a description to the things that had hurled great doubts and fears at her small mind she had the words to describe what it had all been like that's why she felt it was so important to write a book to explain for as her teacher said she was in a position to help others real experience ably described was worth a ton of suppositions by well-meaning experts what hurt so much was the widely-held thought that students of psychiatry seemed to hold if you were silent you could not understand if you didn't use language you couldn't express any thoughts but how did they know a lot of speechless people had heads full of beautiful expressive language that they couldn't use because no one had found the key to their confidence

Here was a window into the mind of someone who was totally isolated, as was my son. Caroline was intelligent, she thought and felt as others did, but without the link with the rest of the world we call communication. She seemed strange and out of step with those around her, inaccessible and inexplicable unless enormous efforts were made to bridge the gap between herself and others.

I was fascinated by what Jennifer told me of Caroline. Caroline was a person with potential locked inside her genes. By her own admission, she cut herself off from the outside world because of her extreme fear. Fear of what, and why? No one is born fearful. Fear is a response to something in the environment. Jennifer believed that Sam – like other autistic children – had a huge backlog of anger, hidden behind a wall of fear. In burying this anger he had cut himself off from all feeling, and so, being unable to experience emotion in the normal way, was unable to respond or communicate. It was possible, she said, to tear down this barrier he had erected; to go back to square one and start again. She said that although his development was now very retarded Sam still had the potential to develop normally.

For me Jennifer's words assumed the luminosity of a bright star in a dark sky. Everything she said sounded logical, and believable in terms of my own experience. Of course the therapy itself was a complete unknown. It did not relate to anything else that either Peter or I knew anything about, and it required an act of faith to assume that it would help our son. But Jennifer said that it would make him better and we were happy to believe her.

Like most parents of autistic children, we had experienced frustration and disillusionment in our attempts to get help for our child. The doctors we encountered did not appear to have any real understanding of the nature or cause of Sam's condition, and gradually it dawned on us that they did not have any hope of curing him either. When he did not get better as everybody hoped he would, we found that attempts to modify the more extreme aspects of his behaviour were the only treatment available for our son. Holding therapy offered us a possible way out of the maze of despair and uncertainty.

So we began the therapy. Each Saturday morning we met Jennifer at the community centre where she hired a room for our purpose. We had to drive a long way to get there. When we arrived at the centre the room would be unlocked and Jennifer would be waiting for us. While Peter went to buy the coffee, I helped Jennifer unroll the mattress which covered half the floor of our tiny room. The remaining floor area was taken up by a table, two chairs and an electric fire. The walls were salmon pink, but stained and grubby. Sunlight sometimes streamed in through the upper half of the barred window; the lower half was frosted glass, protecting us from the stares of passers-by, whose interest must surely have been attracted by the weird noises emanating from our room. It was spartan and dusty, but this room soon became the most secure point in my life. Jennifer was in charge here. She told us what to do. When Peter came back with the coffee we sat chatting for twenty minutes or so, while Sam went through the bag of toys Jennifer always brought with her. Then would come the inevitable 'Well, shall we start?' I was always nervous at the beginning of a session – I felt the onus was on me to make it work. Peter sat some distance away, Jennifer was on the floor beside me. She often became physically involved – holding Sam's arms around me as he tried to pull away, turning his face towards me as he tried to twist his head to the side.

Sam and I lay together on the mattress. I held him firmly so that he could not escape, then turning his face towards me I followed his gaze in an attempt to engage him in eye contact. 'Are you angry with Mummy?' I would ask. 'Tell me how you feel. Show me your anger.' I sometimes glimpsed panic in his eyes – but this was soon obliterated by a cold, glassy gaze as he slipped again behind his autistic defence.

It was like playing a game of cat and mouse wearing a blindfold. I didn't really know what I was doing or what I was dealing with, despite the fact that by this time I had read one or two psychology books and had talked at length with Jennifer about our aims. I just believed that what we were doing was right. Jennifer's argument was simple and the logic indisputable. Sam was psychologically cut off from the world and had barricaded himself behind a wall. I must break through that wall and free him.

Yet the complexity and violence of the emotions aroused in me during these sessions should have alerted me to the fact that there was more to all this than was apparent. For one thing, the pain caused by Sam's continual rejection made me want to run away myself, to cut off. I often felt anxious to escape, but also duty-bound to continue. This must have presented Sam with a most confusing and frightening conflict. My words insisted always that I loved and wanted to help him, but my body language and flickering gaze must have communicated that I felt otherwise. Sometimes I hated him. Sometimes I feared him. But occasionally there were moments of real contact between us. It was at those times that I began to see the possibility of genuine mother-child love developing between the two of us, and this helped me believe I must persist with the therapy. It was impossible to follow the thread of cause and effect in such an intense and complicated emotional situation. It seemed to me that at the beginning of each session we slipped into either an upward or a downward spiral, probably determined by a whole range of factors present before we began.

When we were sucked downward it felt as though Sam and I were sealed off from each other right from the start. My longing to escape the pain and rejection during these sessions was almost overwhelming and I felt sheer panic at the impossibility of doing so. Sam would recede further and further as the minutes ticked by. For two hours I battered relentlessly against the closed door he presented. It felt as though I was beating my head against a brick wall. By the end of such a session I was shattered and hopeless – Sam was tense, and more withdrawn than ever.

It was when we were drawn into the upward spiral that I would sometimes see hope in the distance. Even these sessions were hard going, but at least there was some communication between us. My attempts to verbalize the emotions he might be feeling, combined with the intimacy of eye contact between us, seemed to make it possible for Sam to release his angry feelings. He would scream and kick, pushing me away and pulling my hair – a real tornado. But at least he was responding; at least he was alive. If I coped and enabled him to feel that it was all right for him to express his feelings in this way, his screams would gradually subside. After such an emotional explosion Sam would be exhausted, but content. He would lie in my arms and look at me – sometimes even smile – just like a normal child.

I was always aware of Peter watching us when we did the therapy, but from a greater and greater distance as the weeks went by. His feelings seemed to oscillate between discomfort and barely disguised anger. We had fallen into the habit of lunching in a pub or café after our session, then wandering through the unfamiliar streets of the town or along the banks of the river running through its centre. Sometimes we would eat in a fish and chip restaurant, which Sam loved. He could be quite joyful on these occasions and would eat an enormous meal. I felt optimistic and took pleasure in the fact that I was at last beginning to enjoy a relationship with my son. Increasingly, however, I began to worry about Peter's unhappy state. He was often irritable and uncommunicative after the therapy and his mood would blacken as the afternoon wore on. Theoretically Peter wanted Sam to get better and felt the therapy was helping his son. But emotionally he was confused, bitterly resenting the time and attention being lavished upon Sam, yet unable to say so. Jennifer had told Peter and me that Sam would improve dramatically within six months if we continued with the therapy, stopped arguing, and learned to understand and support each other more. This, however, was easier said than done, for our problems were deep-rooted.

Peter became very depressed. Sometimes he seemed irrational, telling me I would have to 'pay', though for what he was unable to say. After several months I suggested he might prefer not to come in with us during the therapy; he seemed relieved. At this point Jennifer felt it would benefit Sam most if she was to spend some time talking with Peter and me about our problems. So it was decided that the first part of our session would be set aside for discussion, then Peter would go off by himself while Sam and I continued with the holding therapy.

Despite everything, Peter and I were cheered by the fact that Sam had begun to use a few words. Only half a dozen or so, very infrequently, and only as labels – but it was something. Sam had also begun to communicate more freely by gesture. Like most autistic children, he was learning to convey his needs by non-verbal means. If he wanted something that was beyond his reach he would pull me into position then throw my hand towards the desired object. By subtle methods I still do not quite understand he taught me to anticipate his needs and do what he wanted with little apparent prompting on his part.

It is easy to slip into colluding with an autistic child. For example, Sam would always walk slightly behind me so that I would have to keep glancing back to check that he was still following me. If he had fallen too far behind I would adjust my pace accordingly, until we ended up walking at a snail's pace. This was so irritating I would drift off into my own thoughts, then suddenly realize we had stopped altogether. One mother I knew was persuaded by her autistic son that he still needed to be wheeled about in a pushchair at seven years of age. There was no reason for her to do this, other than the fact that the child made her feel that it was necessary. Sam may well have achieved the same result had his pushchair not been stolen when he was four. Fortunately we could not afford to buy him another.

We continued with the holding therapy, and assumed any small progress Sam made to be a result of it. But his few words, his increased communicativeness, his developing relationship with me might all have occurred anyway. We shall never know. But one benefit that definitely accrued from our relationship with Jennifer was that she put me in touch with reading material I would never have come across otherwise.

In particular she told me about a recently published book, *Autistic Children – New Hope for a Cure*, by N. and E. A. Tinbergen. Niko Tinbergen had studied animal behaviour for many years before turning his attention to autism. He analysed the non-verbal behaviour of autistic children by applying the methods he had evolved in his research with animals. Tinbergen argues that autism is an anxiety-dominated emotional imbalance, an emotional derailment, which seriously impairs the child's ability to interact with the environment. Being an ethologist, Tinbergen had developed the valuable skill of observing animals unobtrusively in their natural habitat and then carefully recording those observations. Using this method, he studied autistic children over a long period of time and in many different situations. Tinbergen does not perform tests or present hunches as proven facts. Instead he scrutinizes autistic behaviour as a whole, and attempts to construct a plausible hypothesis to explain the apparently diverse abnormalities of autism.

I found his book fascinating. Reading Niko Tinbergen's detailed descriptions of the mechanisms of behaviour, I felt a new world was being revealed to me. Although I had always been a 'person watcher', the intricate complexity of human behaviour had seemed like a closed door; now I was peering in through the keyhole.

Could it be that there were reasons – understandable reasons – that explained not only Sam's unwillingness to communicate but also his mannerisms and postures? These movements and stances had always worried me. Sam's body was perfectly normal. He was a healthy, good-looking child, yet often his body looked strangely distorted and almost spastic. He would sometimes stand with his two hands held up in a grasping position in front of his chest, like a dog begging for food. Or he would hold his hand stiff and gaze at it, or hunch his shoulders in a tense, unnatural sort of way. These habits, familiar to us, yet totally mysterious, fell into the category of what Tinbergen describes as conflict behaviour.

Conflict behaviour occurs when two (or more) behavioural systems are aroused at the same time. Of particular relevance to autism, says Tinbergen, is the conflict between the desire to approach and explore a person or object and the desire to avoid or withdraw from it lest it be harmful. When these two types of behaviour are evoked simultaneously, then what results is a motivational conflict. This conflict causes behaviour that seems unexplainable to the untrained eye. As the approach and avoidance systems battle for supremacy – and to some extent negate each other – a sort of weird non-behaviour results. How well I remembered Sam's one-step-forwards-one-step-backwards routine. It chilled my blood to learn that one of the earliest manifestations of such conflict was the head-shaking we had found so odd and yet so endearing in Sam's first year.

But why should autistic children suffer more than others from conflicting feelings? After all, most children are brought up in less than perfect surroundings, yet learn to take the rough with the smooth. Tinbergen explains that autistic children do not have the strong social bond with their mothers which provides the 'security umbrella' of psychological protection that allows negative feelings to be coped with and normal development to take place. This can be due to a variety of reasons. But whatever the cause of this initial failure, a child who does not have a secure bond with his mother is vulnerable. Venturing forth from an already precarious position causes such children great anxiety, yet the urge to explore and make social contact is still strong. Hence the withdrawal-dominated motivational conflict, which Tinbergen sees as the primary cause of autism.

We all acknowledge certain activities like nail-biting, foot-tapping or nervous tics as indications that we are suffering from stress. Tinbergen describes how behaviour initially recognizable as anxiety can become changed, how long-lasting intense conflict causes such movements to be formalized or 'frozen' in such a way that they are no longer recognizable, and appear bizarre and puzzling. Sam's 'hands held like claws' posture, for instance, is seen typically, though fleetingly, in a toddler as he reaches for an object. In the autistic child this infantile movement, like so many others, has got 'stuck' between the desire to grasp something and fear of doing so. The shaking movement of the head – a gesture common to many human cultures – is an alternation of two ways of turning the head away from a rejected situation, first in one direction, then in the other. When a young baby indulges excessively in such head-shaking this may indicate that the child is troubled – as I'm sure was the case with Sam. He was already practising a sort of ritualized rejection.

Peter also read *Autistic Children – New Hope for a Cure* with great interest. Despite the conflicts within our relationship we had up to this point been united in our desire to understand and help Sam. But some of the questions raised by this book had alarming implications and Peter found them difficult to cope with. If we accepted that a child can develop autistic traits in response to his environment then there was no escaping the fact that we were to some extent responsible for Sam's condition. As far as I was concerned Sam's actions spoke for themselves. Our son rejected all human contact, preferring the comfort of his tiny, limited world to the risks involved in relating to other people. He was unwilling to look at a human face, let alone look anyone in the eyes. Even the heads of his small dolls had to be torn off before he would allow them into his doll's house. Peter and I felt weighed down by guilt.

As I read I began to discern the link between Sam's previously inexplicable mannerisms and the events of his short life. Tinbergen describes how in certain circumstances mother and child can become caught in a self-reinforcing downward spiral, in which either or both learn to withdraw from the other to protect themselves from further experiencing the pain resulting from initial rejection. Peter and I had ourselves both learned to adopt cutting-off behaviour as a means of dealing with the pain that originated in our own childhoods. It was hardly surprising Sam did the same, albeit in a more extreme and destructive form.

Ironically, the more involved I became in Niko Tinbergen's book the less guilty I felt. It was not our fault, I began to see, that things had happened as they did. Autism resulted not from one or two traumatic events but from a combination of circumstances, and we had been unlucky. Sam and I had got off to a bad start through circumstances beyond our control. Perhaps my extreme anxiety during pregnancy had caused him to be vulnerable even before he was born. I was miserable during my stay in hospital, and worried when I came out. I was hurt by Peter's inability to give me any emotional support. I was isolated and I soon became depressed. Peter and I were both lonely, yet too dependent upon each other. Many of our specific circumstances were described by Tinbergen in his list of 'potentially autismogenic factors', that is, factors that when occurring together would tend to elicit autistic behaviour in a vulnerable child.

I wanted Peter to see these things too. I loved him. I felt the pain he suffered in attempting to repress his feelings and wanted him to ease the burden of guilt that he carried. But he could not bear to face the horrors behind the closed door of his emotions. And so Peter remained angry, without really understanding why.

Although when I first read *Autistic Children – New Hope for a Cure* I did not absorb more than a small amount of what Tinbergen said, his words had a profound effect upon me. I learned something about behaviour, but more important was the monumental status that the book assumed in my mind. Towards the end there is a chapter about holding therapy, written by the American doctor Jennifer had visited – Martha Welch. After reading this I felt that Niko Tinbergen's book was a written testament to the efficacy of holding therapy. He explores many of the different procedures for treating autism and many of the treatments he considers to be helpful – but he feels holding therapy to be the most successful, and able to offer the promise inherent in the book's title.

Tinbergen endorses the theories and methods of Martha Welch; Dr Welch was the source of Jennifer's inspiration. I felt that there could be no doubting Jennifer's word when her ideas had such authoritative backing.

Jennifer had by this time become involved in many aspects of our lives. I remember how when we first met her Peter and I had wondered at Jennifer's concern for our plight and her willingness to help us. Financial gain was obviously not her motive – she charged us so little for her therapy. 'Perhaps she is writing a book about autism,' we thought, 'or perhaps it is just that we are such interesting people that she finds us fascinating.'

I am sure Jennifer really did want to help, but years later I discovered that it actually takes many years of training to qualify as a therapist. Learning to handle other people's emotions without becoming involved and helping others to alter their behaviour without issuing instructions are complex and difficult skills and take a long time to acquire. But Jennifer took on the herculean task of trying to solve my emotional entanglements, and Peter's, single-handed, without such training. She told us to ring her whenever we had a problem, which was often. She advised us by word and sometimes by letter. On occasion I would come downstairs in the morning to find two envelopes, addressed to Peter and myself in Jennifer's neat, pretty handwriting, lying on the doormat. How promising they looked, how full of good intentions. Her letters were written in a warm and friendly tone, but were basically a list of instructions to Peter and me about how we should behave.

Years later I looked back in horror at what she did. Nobody can make good an unhappy relationship by telling people what to say to each other – but Jennifer tried to do just that. I eventually discovered that one of the things I did not like about holding therapy was this assumption by the therapist of the right to issue instructions regarding somebody else's behaviour. Telling a person what to do does not help them to learn how to do it.

One of the biggest practical problems in our household was the fact that Sam still had no proper sleep routine. Things had improved slightly for a time, but were now as bad as ever again. We were all exhausted, physically and emotionally. Once again Jennifer leapt into the breach. Sam was afraid of being alone, she said, and would sleep better if he was in the same room as us.

She came to our house to assess the situation, then explained how we should make up a small bed for Sam next to our own so that we could sleep together as one big happy family. I felt ambivalent about Jennifer's suggestion, and I think Peter was furious – but we were desperate enough to try anything. Before long we both deeply regretted having done so.

After a week or two of more restful nights a whole new set of problems began to emerge. Sam snored. He climbed into our bed, where he thrashed about kicking. Peter often moved next door, just to have some sleep, while I felt completely locked into the over-dependent relationship I had with Sam, from which I now had no respite at all. This new sleeping arrangement became the final straw as far as Peter was concerned. He was explosive. He would seem calm and reasonable while there were other people around but when we were alone he became a tyrant – angry and accusing.

I learned to pretend. I never told anyone about the way Peter behaved towards me and Sam. I accepted Peter's mood swings, and felt that I must be somehow to blame. One day we were driving home – we were about four miles from our house. Sam, as ever, sat silent in the back. As I drove Peter became more and more angry about an incident that had occurred that afternoon. I was frightened of being alone with him and said I was going to stop at a friend's house, thinking this would give him time to cool off. He lost his temper and pulled on the hand-brake. We lurched to a halt – the car following crashed into the back of us. The driver behind was furious, Peter was shouting, I was crying. Sam was goodness knows where. Sam was no doubt terrified. Sam was lost.

This sort of incident was not unusual. Sometimes I try to imagine how life must have been for Sam then. Both Jennifer and I were constantly telling him that he must drop his defences and experience the real world. But what a frightening and unstable world it was. One of the worst aspects as far as his relationship with his father was concerned must have been the fact that Peter was so unpredictable. Sometimes kind and loving, sometimes angry and resentful. Tinbergen describes how some parents of autistic children relate to their child in an intensive love-hate manner, a kind of 'psychological child battering'. My behaviour must have also confused Sam, gravitating as it did between intense love and apparent indifference when I became preoccupied by my own worries.

The strain between Peter and me was reflected in Sam's behaviour. Any initial benefits he had derived from the therapy were being masked by acute anxiety. He ground his teeth in an alarming manner or made a loud cutting-off noise like an electrical hum. He picked obsessively at grass and carpets, or anything from which he could pull bits. Jennifer said that we must continue with the therapy or Sam would be worse off than when we started. She asked Peter to write about his feelings during the week, and give her his notes at the weekend. She must have had some shocks.

But still we continued with the holding, and with Jennifer's version of family therapy. In fact Peter would have needed a great deal of professional therapeutic support to cope with the resentment he felt towards me and Sam, as well as the anger he was being forced to confront as a result of holding therapy. Jennifer obviously did not see this. She led us into deeper waters than we could safely cope with.

Jennifer always encouraged Peter and me to express our emotions, but I felt that tampering with such primitive feelings was dangerous. Harrowing experiences such as our holding sessions were can tap directly into disturbing childhood memories and unleash violent emotions. Peter seemed to hover on the brink of mental collapse; I was always afraid that his emotional eruptions would become a full-scale volcano. I was intermittently frightened and depressed. Life seemed precarious. By luck we managed to avoid harming each other physically, and to get through this difficult and dangerous time.

Like so many people looking for a peg on which to hang their unhappiness, Peter decided that our house was to blame. It was too small. It had cost us too much in blood, sweat and tears, he felt, and held too many unhappy memories.

Our tiny cottage had come a long way from the cold uninhabitable shell we had moved into four years earlier. In the kitchen, now red-tiled and welcoming, our Aga throbbed like a great warm heart. The rest of the house was carpeted and cosy. Our lovely view lay safely behind double glazing and was prettily framed by stripped pine architrave. Roses climbed around the front door; honeysuckle wafted in from the back. It was difficult to believe that life inside could be so miserable.

The idea of selling our house broke my heart, but we had to

do something. We could not go on as we were, and I thought perhaps Peter was right about the bad associations. So we began house-hunting. Several months and many bitter arguments later we found somewhere. It was a Victorian stone semi – renovated, decorated and ready to live in. I photographed my beautiful garden, took one last look across the valley and handed over my dream to a schoolteacher, who bought it for the view.

7

SCHOOL

By the time we moved into our new house Sam had been going to school for a year and a half. It was impossible for me to see him objectively but his teacher felt he had made great improvement. He was being taught sign language and had so far acquired two signs – one for drink and one for toilet. He had also begun to imitate animal noises.

Sam's yearly report from school stated that at four and a half his physical skills were around the two and a half to three year level and that his gait was still clumsy. He was said to relate to the adults around him but not to the other children. He was also described as having good eye contact, which I found suprising, as it seemed to me that he hardly ever looked anyone in the eye. His play was still at an exploratory level and he rarely used 'pretend' play. It was acknowledged that Sam understood some of what was said to him – how much was never agreed upon – although he often failed to respond and even less frequently made any attempt to communicate himself.

I was never happy about Sam's learning sign language; it seemed pointless. He could learn a word as easily as he could learn a sign and I felt that what was lacking in Sam was the desire to communicate, not the ability to understand the symbols. This was one thing about which Mrs Stanley and I disagreed. There were others. Although indulgent at first and perfectly willing to allow Sam a settling-in period, she had begun to feel that he should be discouraged from carrying his hard object around with him. There was some sense in what Mrs Stanley said. As she pointed out, Sam was often having to function with the use of only one hand – his other hand being occupied with clutching his object. It seemed to me, however, that his object-carrying was somehow connected with his security. He appeared to need an object in his hand – the panic he showed if it was mislaid was evidence enough of that. Sam's idiosyncrasy that bothered Mrs Stanley most was his habit of carrying a small book in the taxi with him when he travelled between home and school. He would hand over the book when he got to school, then collect it when he was coming home. To me it seemed that he used it as a sort of linking device. But Mrs Stanley did not approve, and Sam was for a time made to manage without his 'go-between' object. The repercussions came immediately. Sam developed an obsession whereby he felt himself unable to enter the schoolroom. He would get to the doorway, then find himself unable to cross the threshold unless Mrs Stanley came over and touched him. I saw this only once. As he stood there with his foot poised yet unable to break through the invisible barrier that sealed off the schoolroom, it reminded me of when he had felt prevented from eating or drinking – how he had lifted the food to his mouth yet been unable to get it inside – when he had been frightened by the removal of his drinking spout. His 'carrying' object was reinstated.

As well as Mrs Stanley there was a nursery helper called Shirley permanently attached to Sam's class. She played finger games and sang with the children, and encouraged riotous rough-and-tumble games which Sam loved. He became very fond of her. I will never forget the first time we ran into Shirley outside school. It was at our local garden centre. 'Hello, Sam,' she said in her jolly voice. Sam was absolutely astonished. He looked thunderstruck. He threw himself into his touching routine, which involved touching Shirley then looking hard at me to get me to say her name over and over – he needed to affirm and reaffirm that it was indeed who he thought it was. Then he did his linking routine – first my hand was placed in Shirley's arm then her hand upon mine. I think he would really have liked us to embrace each other.

The numbers in Sam's class varied between about four and ten children. It was a shifting population – rarely was a child in the group for more than nine months, and usually their stay was much shorter. The children were meant to be assessed, usually statemented (the preparation of an official document of the assessment), then moved on to the school considered most appropriate to their needs. Sam posed something of a problem as nobody was sure where he ought to go. He had been diagnosed autistic by Elizabeth Newson and certainly showed the classic autistic symptoms. But Mrs Stanley did not think he was autistic and I was chastised for wanting a label for him.

The gap between Mrs Stanley's view of Sam's condition and my own was ever-widening. Mrs Stanley considered Sam to be both communicative and very willing to learn, but prevented from doing so by his handicap. I considered that the very nature of his handicap was his lack of desire to communicate and his consequent inability to learn. We might well have been discussing different children.

Our relationship was not helped by my involvement with Jennifer Stonecross. Both through talking with Jennifer and through reading *Autistic Children – New Hope for a Cure* I had come to believe that Sam's retarded development – his learning difficulties and his behaviour problems – resulted from failed bonding and his consequent withdrawal from the world around him. Such ideas were beyond Mrs Stanley's experience and she simply did not want to know about them. Mrs Stanley held the behaviourist's view of children like Sam: you should treat what you could see and if the child did something undesirable you dissuaded him from doing it again by associating his action with something unpleasant, such as being made to stand in a corner or leave the room. This approach takes no account of why the child behaves as he does and, in my experience, if he is prevented from indulging in one form of aberrant behaviour he usually then just resorts to another. However I was not aware of the diversity of opinion regarding the nature and cause of autism. I did not realize that Mrs Stanley was adopting a behaviourist stance or that I had a more psychoanalytical point of view. (Behaviourism is a school of psychology that regards objective, observable aspects of behaviour as the only valid subject for study. Psychoanalysis is a method of studying the mind and treating mental and emotional disorders based on revealing and investigating the role of the unconscious mind.) I could only ponder the chasm between Mrs Stanley's perception of Sam and my own.

Jennifer and I decided that it would be helpful if she was to visit

Sam's school and explain what we were trying to do with holding therapy. During her visit she attempted to convince the staff that Sam had the potential for normal development although he now seemed retarded. Mrs Stanley was not impressed. She became quite antagonistic towards me and clearly resented my interference and my peculiar ideas. I felt out on a limb, with nobody but Jennifer Stonecross to cling to.

After the initial honeymoon period at school when Sam was said to be doing so well, problems began to appear. Sam started masturbating. He would throw himself face downwards on to the floor and rub against the carpet, working himself into a frenzy. Or he would rub himself against the furniture to achieve the same effect. Although our reasons may have been different, Mrs Stanley, Jennifer and I agreed that Sam should not continue this activity. My worry was that he would seize upon it as the perfect means for cutting off from those around him – it provided a pleasurable sensation and kept him cocooned in his isolated world – and that he would masturbate to the exclusion of everything else if allowed to do so. I used to tell him to 'stop wriggling', for that was what he appeared to be doing as he lay flat on his face with his bottom moving from side to side. I think that Mrs Stanley adopted more restrictive measures, but between us we managed to keep Sam's habit under control most of the time.

One of the advantages offered by Sam's school was the chance to meet parents of other children in his class at the regular parent-teacher meetings. I was nervous the first few times and said very little, but gradually I came to see how things were. The purpose of the meetings, it seemed to me, was limited to making the parents feel better. Each of us took it in turn to talk about our child. Sometimes staff offered helpful suggestions but mostly it was just commiseration with an absolute insistence that we must not think that our child's problems were anything to do with us. We were told not to blame ourselves for what appeared to be seen as a blow that fate had dealt, rather than anything over which we had any control. This seemed silly to me. As many of the children in Sam's class were acknowledged as being emotionally disturbed, it seemed obvious that their difficulties must have at least something to do with their home environment. The teachers were so anxious to avoid apportioning blame that they ended up by saying very little that was of practical use. This made me angry because I felt that my family needed constructive help, not hollow reassurance.

There was usually at least one other 'autistic type' child in Sam's group, and I was always eager to hear about the experiences of their families and how they dealt with problems that were similar to my own. It seemed that these children almost always had dreadful sleeping problems just like Sam. There were often the same difficulties with obsessional and cutting-off behaviour, although some parents did not describe it like that. One little boy who looked completely normal yet was apathetic and seemed 'absent' for most of the time was described at the end of his assessment period as 'severely retarded'. His mother spoke no English and so probably did not understand much of what went on during the meeting, but her husband seemed devoted to his son and quite desperate to help him. I longed to say to this man I was sure his son understood what was being said, but I was too inhibited to do so. This child seemed to me in many ways like Sam, only more so. His limbs were flaccid; he wore a lost expression. He appeared to be suffering from an almighty depression. I heard later that his parents had taken their child back to their native country, which cheered me. Perhaps his mother had failed to cope in a strange land where she did not speak the language, and maybe with the support of her own family and in her natural environment she would be able to persuade her son to abandon his autistic withdrawal and start to live again. At least I hoped that might be the case. Surely he must be better off than he would be in this country in a school for the severely educationally subnormal where, despite the best of intentions, the staff have limited expectations of their pupils and certainly do not expect them to recover.

It had been suggested that Sam might attend such a school. At that time there were two basic types of school for children who could not cope with mainstream education – those for the severely educationally subnormal and those for the moderately educationally subnormal. There were other specialist schools run by the Autistic Society, but these were few and far between. In our area was one of each type of state school and I went to see them both. I came away utterly depressed. The children were obviously much more able at the school for moderate learning difficulties, but the classes were large and I did not think Sam would cope with so little individual help. At the other school the facilities were much better, but I could not bear to think of Sam with such severely handicapped children when those he had mixed with so far were comparatively normal. The autistic children at this school seemed to be left to indulge their obsessions – I watched one child for twenty minutes or so as he sat alone in a corner dangling a piece of string two inches from the end of his nose. I wanted to pull Sam out of his obsessional state, not allow him to sink into it. I did not want him to go to that school. The education department could not force me to send Sam somewhere I felt was inappropriate, so the question of where Sam should go for his future schooling remained for a while unanswered.

Sam seemed to take up every minute of my time – Peter probably felt left out. But on the other hand Peter was rarely at home. He must have realized he was becoming dislocated from Sam but was unsure what to do about it. He decided to visit Sam's school.

Peter went to see Sam at school yesterday and came back depressed because the school feel that Sam is only progressing very slowly. He has also been very disruptive at school for the last week or two. Peter and Sam are very estranged from each other – due I suppose to Peter working such long hours recently. But I think it is also due to Peter seeing the close relationship that is developing between Sam and me. I feel torn between the two. I'm depressed and very worried about Sam.

It seemed as though every step towards Sam was a step away from Peter. I frequently wrote things down in an attempt to understand my feelings:

I felt terrible this morning – completely distanced from Sam and unable to summon up the effort to try and get through to him. Eventually he slept for an hour or so, and seemed much happier and more outgoing when he awoke. This made me feel better. I am still anxious about Peter, though – he seems so miserable and I don't know what to do. After lunch I drove Sam down to the river and he had a lovely swing. I remembered that day about two years ago when I took him to that same spot and attempted to play ball with him. I threw the ball and shouted 'Catch, Sam.' He completely ignored me and shuffled off in the other direction. He had only just learned to walk then. I remember feeling so silly. I spent the next half hour throwing the ball and fetching it myself – trying to be two people. At least Sam responds to me now. He looks at me, and will occasionally do as he is asked. I am overjoyed that he likes the swings at last. He also had a slide (went down by himself) and a see-saw, in which I forced myself to include two little girls who wanted to participate. I'm still very nervous when other children approach Sam and me. I feel embarrassed – afraid they will notice there is something wrong with Sam, and worried that I will not be able to cope with them. After a while (I forced myself to persist for a few minutes) I made Sam get off the see-saw. He seemed resentful. We walked along the river and he started picking grass which I hate. I was upset and tried talking to him. This seemed to help. We walked up through the trees – he stopped picking and became much more relaxed.

As I watched him I started thinking about my own childhood. I thought about autism in relation to myself. It made me desperately sad to think of the way I was as a young child – and have been intermittently ever since – which was withdrawn and at times practically mute, yet furious that people thought me stupid. And now I've passed it on to Sam only much much worse. Recalling how I used to feel makes it possible for me to think that Sam might also understand what he hears – a horrifying thought when I think of what he has heard. I remember the frustration of not being attributed with much intelligence. Although I understood a great deal about the nature of things and people I did not seem to have a store of 'facts', and so appeared terribly ignorant the whole time. Perhaps it is like this for Sam.

When it suddenly occurred to me during this walk that Sam might be suffering as I had done, I felt a strong empathy with him. But this was coloured by a mixture of resentment, anger, sympathy and guilt. To make things even more difficult the pressure forcing Sam and me together came from all sides. Peter was rejecting us both, and neither Sam nor I had anyone else to turn to apart from each other. Jennifer was constantly urging me towards closer involvement with Sam. I believed then this was what Sam needed and I felt that I should spend every minute with him. What I did not understand was that I was using him for support far more than he was able to use me. I started bringing Sam home from school early, collecting him just after lunch, in the mistaken belief that more time spent with me would mean more support for him. At first he seemed to like the new arrangement.

It's lovely collecting Sam early from school. Thank goodness I passed my driving test and so am able to do this now. Mrs Stanley does not approve – when I get Sam out of the door it is almost like stealing him from her. He seems happy at home with me. I try to involve him more now – he puts washing in the dryer, etc. When we go outside I try talking to him more. It is normally so difficult when we are in the garden, but today when he picked the grass I talked to him. He kept looking at me to see what I would do, then he stopped. We managed this for about half an hour, which is enough. Later on this afternoon I took him down to the paddling pool. I love to see him in amongst the other children. He has made hardly any stupid noises today and there has been virtually no teeth-grinding.

Mrs Stanley might not approve of me taking Sam home early, but Jennifer Stonecross was delighted. Life for me was too black and white in those days. Mrs Stanley did not understand Sam – she was therefore bad; Jennifer said that Sam would get better – so she was good. I had no confidence or belief in my own ability to make reasonable decisions, and especially where Sam was concerned.

The hot-house intensity of the relationship between Sam and me increased further when we were snowed in for a week. The outside world ceased to exist as Sam and I hung on to each other like the last two survivors in an icy wasteland. I remembered the last time that we had been isolated by the weather which was when Sam was a baby. 'Things are much better now,' I thought to myself. Such is the need for hope. I clung like a limpet to the belief that Sam was getting better and that I was in control of my life. In fact things were worse than ever, and Sam and I were suffering from the emotional claustrophobia of our relationship.

He started pulling away from me and once again making extreme overtures towards his father. Although Sam always had his autistic defence as a means of escape, he probably longed for a more normal means of counterbalancing my demanding attempts at mothering. If only Peter had been able to reciprocate, and offer his son the emotional involvement and support he so craved. But Peter was controlled by his conflicting feelings. He often rejected Sam – which made me furious – but at other times he would really try to communicate with his son.

Peter was in the habit of playing his harmonica in the bath each evening, and as he and Sam often shared their bath, Sam had come to think of harmonica-playing as the thing that he and his father did together. He would try to play himself, and soon adopted the harmonica as a symbol of togetherness between himself and Peter. I wrote in my diary:

> Last Saturday Sam was obsessed by the harmonica. He kept pulling Peter off on his own to play with him and closing the door behind them. It's good to see him so keen to learn something – and to see him wanting to be with his father. If I try to enter the room Sam pushes me out and closes the door. He wants to be alone with his father, and perhaps to show me that he has other strings to his bow besides me.

> At first Peter seemed pleased that Sam was showing a preference for him, but by Sunday he was fed up with the game and started pushing Sam away. Today they played a bit in the bath but Sam's great enthusiasm has gone. Several times he threw the harmonica at the wall. I think he was hurt by Peter's rejection – their special 'playing the harmonica together' activity has been spoiled. Later on when Peter put him to bed it took Sam more than an hour to fall asleep. He was making loud throaty noises and Peter got angry. Sam got upset. I felt desperate but dared not intervene. The tension in this house sometimes seems unbearable.

We were all near to breaking point. By the time we moved out of our cottage both Peter and I were way beyond regretting what we were leaving behind. We were keen for a change in our circumstances and pinned all our hopes on the new house. For a time we were happier – we had much more space, a house that was warm and easy to live in, and what seemed like friendly accommodating neighbours close by. As before, we all slept together in the largest bedroom – Peter and I in the double bed and Sam in his small bed next to us. Peter went away for a week, which gave me a chance to settle things in our new house. Perhaps, I thought, everything would be all right after all. Unfortunately everything was not all right. Our relationship was a disaster, and Peter and I both knew it. Our son was emotionally very disturbed, whichever way you looked at it. Whether he had been born with a handicap or not, he had certainly been damaged in the last five and a quarter years.

Sam was still afraid of being by himself. If left alone he became very distressed and ground his teeth and threw toys or tried to follow the nearest adult. He was still not able to speak. Although he had acquired a few words of sign language this had not helped him towards spoken language as his teachers had hoped. He hardly verbalized at all – the few words he did use were labels and these were applied only after a great deal of persuasive prompting. Sam could neither read nor write. He played very little – and then it was nothing more complex than running a car along his road or putting his saucepan on the cooker. According to his teacher Sam had the ability to learn to recognize symbols, but I could never get him to attend long enough to attempt any such structured activity.

Peter and I had tried everything that we could think of to help repair our relationship. Although we had moved house in an attempt to make a fresh start things were now as bad as ever. I asked a friend to come and stay.

Sue came for the weekend, which was lovely. A welcome break. Sam is very relaxed with Sue around. I think he realizes she understands and sympathizes with some of his problems. She also relaxes me. Peter was awful which made me furious. Whenever he shouts Sam starts grinding his teeth. Having Sue here made me realize how tense I am much of the time – either waiting for something to happen or smarting from something that Peter has done or said.

The day after Sue left I cried for a long time. Then I rang Peter at work and asked him to look for somewhere else to live. He agreed. He never came back again, except as a visitor.

8

ALL ALONE

So here I was – alone with my autistic child. I was terrified. I assumed that in the short term, at least until we had decided what to do, Peter would take care of us financially, and he did. My more immediate concern was emotional survival. I felt abandoned, rejected, afraid of the past and even more afraid of the future. I doubted my ability to look after Sam on my own, even though this was more or less what I had been doing for the past year. My main worry was the idea of there not being anybody there. I was also frightened that without a third party to act as a tempering influence, Sam and I would become so over-reliant on each other that we would never be able to part or develop as individuals. Also – and this worried me even more – I was angry with Sam.

Peter left yesterday. I think of nothing but Peter, Sam and myself – how we all seem to love and hate each other so violently. I'm afraid of being alone with Sam – afraid of blaming him. From the time he was born I feared he would push Peter away from me. He has done so – my worst fears have been confirmed. I was, and am, completely dependent upon Peter, as is he upon me. Since Sam's birth he has been furious at me for bringing this child between us, and at Sam for being that child.
Now Peter has gone. Yet he and I both adore Sam. We wanted him to have everything we did not have – the love and the security. We have loved him and punished him intermittently since he was born.

I have no idea how these events affected Sam. His behaviour was so strange anyway it was impossible to tell. Was he glad that his father had left? At least it meant that day-to-day life was more settled; the raw emotional state in which we had been living must have been terrifying. Or was he even more frightened now that his emotional base had broken in two? This base had been rocky and insecure, but it was the only one he had. I do not know how he felt. I was so preoccupied by my own fear and misery I hardly even thought about it. When I did I felt Peter was to blame for not being a proper father, and it seemed imperative that he still fulfil certain functions such as being there for special events and holidays when I thought families should be together. Sam needed his father to be there. It never occurred to me that the gaping hole I felt was more for my own loss than it was for Sam's.

Not long after Peter left it was Easter weekend. Easter Monday meant the fair was in town. Sam must go, I decided. Peter agreed and it was decided that we would both take him. Squelchy mud and rancid fat, chips and candy floss and roundabouts – how tacky it all seemed, and how overwhelming. Everywhere I looked were the inevitable happy families, highlighting my own failure and loneliness. Sam wanted nothing – no hot dog, no pop, no doll on a stick. One of the most painful aspects of living with an autistic child is that you cannot give them anything. They do not want anything, apart from the satisfaction of their obsessions. Perhaps the word obsession gives the wrong impression, implying as it does a meaningless ritual with little or no emotional content. Sam's current preoccupation was helicopters, and while it was true that he would carry the object clutched in his hand like a talisman and would fly into a panic if it was dropped or mislaid, there were other times when it seemed to fill him with a great happiness. Then he would smile and stroke the object for which he appeared to feel genuine love.

On one of the roundabouts at the fair we came across a huge red helicopter, complete with spinning rotor blades. Sam was beside himself. He leapt aboard, barely restrainable, even before the roundabout had stopped turning and the previous occupants had vacated their seats. Sam had never been on a roundabout before. I loved watching him spin past with the other children, looking so happy, but was afraid that he would fall off in his excitement as he kept trying to stand up, but he didn't. Sam was almost bursting with joy – he rode that helicopter for a long time. When we did finally extract him from his seat, he was heartbroken. He did not cry – Sam never cried – but he hung on like grim death, leaving us in no doubt about his preference. I think he would like to have stayed there for ever, but once he was back on the ground the spell was broken and our day was soon over. We all had then to face the hard reality of separation as we went our own ways – Peter back to his flat and Sam and I to our empty house.

I found the first enormous obstacle to be overcome in life as a single parent was getting up in the morning. When I was awoken by Sam at about 7 a.m., the day stretched before me endlessly. Weekends were the worst as it was then that my single status loomed largest and I felt most vulnerable. We lived in a middle-class area – the land of educational toys and good relationships. Rain or shine the gardens around our way resounded with the happy shouts of successful parents playing with their well-adjusted children. How I envied those families their completeness, which jogged a memory from my early childhood.

I used to play a game with my dolls in which I would set three or four of them with me to make a happy family. There would always be one doll excluded. She, poor creature, was forever trying to 'get in' to our exclusive circle. She would come around saying she had nowhere else to go or whinging about being alone, but I would always kick her out. My role was a cross between a loving mother who presided over this idyllic family group and fought off intruders, and one of the loved children who felt sorry for this pathetic yet contemptible child nobody wanted. Sam seemed destined to remain forever on the outside. My nightmare was coming to life.

Throughout this turbulent time when Peter and I were trying to separate Jennifer remained closely involved with both of our lives. It was she I telephoned first of all with the news that Peter had left home. She was the last person we had seen as a family, as only days before Peter moved out we had together taken Sam for his therapy. Now that I had to look after Sam on my own, I felt I needed Jennifer's support even more than before. She was literally the only person I had to turn to. I telephoned her often. The long drive to and from the therapy room meant that at least our Saturdays were taken care of, which was a great relief. It provided a sort of backbone to the week. Keeping at bay the huge tide of panic that threatened to engulf me during those first few months on my own was a struggle. The only two hours in the week when I felt safe were those we spent in the therapy room with Jennifer. There I felt looked after, and sane in my belief that Sam was savable and worth saving. The version of the holding therapy we had originally embarked on had all but vanished by this time. In my distraught, fragmented state I could not cope with my own anger, let alone that of my unhappy child directed at me and all the guilt that entailed. My child was psychotic – he was out of touch with reality, he lived in a world of his own – and I was not in a fit state to deal with him. For much of our session Sam was left so sift through Jennifer's bag of toys while she and I talked endlessly. It appals me now to think of some of the things he heard. We treated him as though he had neither eyes nor ears. Then after an hour or so I would guiltily try to 'hold' him – turn his face towards me and insist that he 'show me his feelings'. Had he done so, he would probably have killed me, for I remember how I used to feel when my mother did the same sort of thing to me.

After my father died when I was ten there were several months when my mother dragged me around on a seemingly endless procession of visits to various people. I would be left to sit while she talked – discussing and complaining about my father and about me, and the unfairness of her lot in being saddled with a child to bring up single-handed. She behaved as though I did not exist. I would sit there frightened and alone – hating her but not really daring to think such wicked thoughts. And so I believe it must have been for Sam.

The similarity between those distant events and their re-enactment by myself and my son was striking. Although I had begun to think about the way destructive behaviour patterns are set in early childhood and perpetuated through the whole of life, I was now unconsciously forcing Sam to assume the role that had been mine as a child. The inevitability with which insecure adults go on to produce disturbed children already struck me as tragic – the evidence of it was all around me. Between us my sisters and I have six children and not one of them is really particularly stable. Nor was my mother. Not that she could help this, any more than it was her fault that her children passed on their emotional scars to their own children. But I was depressed to see how emotional deprivation is transmitted from one generation to the next, and how an unlucky individual can – like Sam – fall victim to circumstances. It seemed to me that Sam was the point at which two lines of deprivation met. In both Peter and myself, our 'natural' child-rearing abilities were damaged by our own inadequate upbringings. We came together ill-equipped to manage a relationship of any kind, let alone parenthood.

Although Peter was no longer living at home we were in many ways as involved with each other as ever. The difference was that there were now long enough gaps between his visits for me to start thinking of myself and Sam as having a life apart from his. At first Peter came to visit about twice a week – he baby-sat so I could go out with friends, then came again at the weekend to see Sam. For these weekend visits I usually arranged an outing such as a picnic or a walk in the country. Peter remained as inconsistent as ever. Sometimes he wanted to take Sam off on his own, at other times he was not interested in Sam at all, but wished only to talk to me. Occasionally we had lovely days out together, but as often as not they would dissolve into a row when Peter was about to leave. Often it seemed to me that I had managed to achieve a calm, happy (though always precarious) balance in my relationship with Sam, only to have it smashed by one of Peter's visits.

Yet I could easily have asked Peter to come less often or not to visit the house, neither of which I did. Peter and I seemed to be still tied together in a mutually destructive relationship. When sometimes I felt that Sam would be better off not seeing Peter I rationalized my continued involvement by telling myself that Sam needed to see his father. And perhaps he did. Sometimes they came back from outings filled with the old joy, and this delighted me. It made all the traumas seem worthwhile.

Three months slipped by and suddenly it was midsummer. We were very short of money by this time so a holiday was out of the question, but Peter's parents asked if we would like to visit them in the south of England for a week. It seemed a good idea and did provide a welcome break. The train journey caused me great anxiety, however.

Sam and I went to stay with Peter's parents last Friday and came back yesterday. They don't relate much to Sam, though of course he is not easy to relate to. I spent most of my evenings upstairs trying to get him to sleep. There was a lot of travelling involved – three train journeys each way – and Sam was mostly very good. Once or twice when he did threaten to become difficult I felt tense and panicky in the way I do when he goes out to play. I feel a sense of great danger, as though dozens of people are watching us, and annihilate us by their watching. It's exactly the same feeling I used to have about myself, though I don't often have it now except in relation to Sam. It's as though each person who enters the area where we are increases the threat to us, and the closer they are the more threatening. On the train yesterday I felt relieved every time someone got up in our cubicle to leave their seat. I can't help noticing that this feeling of panic affects Sam and I try hard to control it. If only I could stop being so aware of other people and just relate to Sam. On this occasion I managed to avoid him getting out of control, but felt completely drained and exhausted.

Later that summer a friend came with her young daughter to stay with us for a few days. Like me, Christine was a single parent. She and Jessie's father had split up soon after Jessie's birth, and I could not help but compare our situations. Bringing up a baby on her own cannot have been easy for Christine, but she had devoted herself exclusively to the task. She had decided early on that her relationship with Jessie's father would not work and that she and her daughter would be better off on their own. Her daughter was fatherless, but she did not bear the emotional scars that crippled my son. The difference between three-year-old Jessie and nearly-six-year-old Sam was staggering. Jessie was bright, outgoing and talkative; Sam was anxious, withdrawn and mute. Once I had got over the shock of the inevitable comparison between our two children I began to notice the difference between the way Christine treated Jessie and the way I behaved with Sam. She seemed to be acutely aware of Jessie, sometimes to the exclusion of everything else. Even when she was talking with me she seemed to have an eye on what Jessie was doing, and when Jessie came to her or needed something Christine was there to help or sooth or commiserate. My attitude towards Sam was quite different. When there were other people present I was always so worried about what they thought of us that I paid little heed to Sam's needs – as had happened on our train journey. We were either welded together in our insular, impenetrable world, or locked in our own prisons – a million miles from each other. We had never been like Christine and Jessie – not the first month, the first day or the first hour. I had rarely before had the chance to observe such a successful mother-child relationship. It surprised me as I did not know it could be like that.

Those who believe that autism is an organic condition would say that an autistic baby fails to elicit a normal response from its mother because it is withdrawn from birth. But how can a new-born baby be withdrawn? A baby's range of social responses is extremely limited when compared with those of an adult; the developing relationship between the two is therefore far more dependent upon the mother's behaviour than that of her infant.

While Christine and Jessie were visiting I found it impossible to do the holding therapy with Sam. I was supposed to hold him for at least an hour each day, without fail, and insist he either maintain eye contact with me or release his angry feelings by shouting. I could not do this when there were other people around us. I became tense and any possibility of lowering my emotional defences or expecting Sam to do so was out of the question. I was losing faith anyway in holding therapy. We had struggled for so long – it had been almost two years – and were, I felt, going around in circles.

On the other hand I had become reliant on Jennifer, and my relationship with her was based on Sam's weekly therapy sessions. Jennifer helped me through this period of my life by simply being there. She encouraged me to talk about Peter and Sam. When we left the therapy room I always felt comforted, and so believed our talks must be helpful. But this was a temporary sort of help – soothing rather than healing. Jennifer was supportive but basically I still felt worthless and handled people and situations in the same self-destructive manner by advertising the fact. I would have to alter my behaviour if I was going to improve my life. Eventually Jennifer gave me the name of a psychotherapist – somebody actually qualified to give me the sort of help she had herself been attempting for the past two years. Of course she could not have known this would lead to my abandoning holding therapy, and my reaching a point from which I looked back in anger at some of the things she had tried to do with us. For the time being, however, we continued our weekly sessions, only now I visited Dr Read once a fortnight for my own therapy.

What a revelation! Dr Read encouraged me to talk about my thoughts and feelings, but how different were these sessions from the shapeless emotional ramblings I had shared with Jennifer. There was more structure here. Dr Read said that it was not her intention to simply prop me up when I felt miserable. She aimed to help me gain the skills I needed to help myself at such times. It was also agreed that the help she provided was for me only, which freed me from the guilt I always felt when talking about myself rather than Sam. She would have considered it unethical anyway to advise about Sam as he was still being treated by Jennifer. However as most of my pressing worries at that time were in some way to do with Sam, she soon came to know all about him. One of the things we looked at in some detail was my inability to stay 'in touch' with Sam when there were other people present. With the help of Dr Read I forced myself to confront this problem by visiting people with Sam, which I found terrifying. Dr Read asked me to write about how I felt on these occasions.

Yesterday Sam and I went to visit some neighbours who were out in the field that they have recently acquired. They have made it into a lovely playground with swings and toys, and while the children play the adults sit around chatting. One of the women has asked me to call in any time with Sam and I have done so once or twice, although we have never stayed for long. I should visit in the field more often as there is plenty of unconfined space which Sam likes and the people there are always friendly, but just entering it makes me nervous. This is partly because everyone usually sits at the far end of the field, which means that Sam and I have to walk about one hundred feet from the gate to reach them. It is like walking across a stage. By the time I do reach them my heart is pounding (with fear, not exertion) and I usually either am struck dumb or say something odd in my embarrassment. When we visited yesterday, however, I felt less nervous than usual, which pleased me. 'Oh good, it's becoming easier,' I thought. I chatted for a few minutes then took Sam over to their paddling pool. There were about eight children milling about. Sam wandered off a few yards playing with a balloon. I was sitting with the other mothers, feeling fairly relaxed for once, when suddenly Sam screamed because his balloon had flown over the fence. I said, 'Come on, Sam, let's get your balloon,' and we left to retrieve it. I walked to the gate with him but then sent him on alone into the next garden to fetch the balloon. He would not normally venture so far from me, and would not have done so on this occasion had he not been keen to get his balloon back. When he returned to the place where he had left me I was not there – I had run into our garage to get something. I was back within a few seconds. Sam seemed slightly upset but I thought nothing of it at the time. Later I realized that it was probably then that he lost his emotional footing. Soon after we got back to the field Sam's balloon burst. He appeared to cope with this but five minutes later he started whimpering and putting his fingers in his mouth – pretending that they were stuck. This 'fingers in the mouth' routine has an obsessive quality -- it is a sign that Sam is not coping. He also does it with toys. He will put a toy in his mouth and bite on it (not very hard, just enough to keep it there), and walk around whimpering with the toy dangling from his mouth. It looks like a sort of stylized display of stressful feelings. He seems to be saying, 'Look what a state I am in. Help. Do something about it.' Unfortunately I am not usually able to do anything helpful, especially when it happens in public. I panic when he behaves in this way and am rarely able to view objectively what is happening until after the event, when it is too late.

When Sam started biting yesterday I tried to jolly him out of it, which sometimes works. I say, 'Come on Sam, it's not stuck. Don't be silly.' I did not know what had upset him. I tried talking to him, taking his fingers from his mouth and sitting him on my knee. Sam kept whimpering and biting his fingers, then started obsessively throwing my hand in the air. I tried to pretend that everything was all right, and to continue my conversation with my neighbour, but soon began to feel angry and tense. Sam was by this time picking grass obsessively so I decided that it was time to go. Sam ran down to the bottom of the field where he stepped up his grass-picking pace and also started grinding his teeth. I said, 'Come on, Sam, we're going home.' He got into a state and threw his aeroplane to the ground. I felt conscious of everybody watching (and judging) me, and my inadequate handling of the situation. I racked my brain to think of what a proper mother would do. For some reason it seemed impossible for me to go to Sam – I was afraid that the other mothers would think that I had been manipulated by my son. Sam started screaming and after a few minutes I did go to him, feeling terrible. He kicked and screamed all the way home. I felt desperate and furious. When we got home I forced myself to tell Sam how angry I was so that I would not bottle it up and take it out on him later.

This incident made me feel an awful sense of failure. I'm worried about what the other people thought of me, and also the fact that I let Sam down dreadfully. Thinking about it later I could see how I mismanaged the whole thing, failing to respond to Sam's signals for help early on, then pulling further away as he became more insistent. But I'm still not sure what I should have done, or when.

Dr Read responded in a friendly but neutral way to my outpourings – neither criticizing me nor encouraging me to feel sorry for myself, but simply accepting what I said. Her questions caused me to think along new lines and to see myself in a new perspective. Probably most important of all, she refused to be drawn into the destructive sort of interaction which was all I had ever known. She would not be cajoled into taking control of me by assuming the role of either judge or comforter, and thereby she forced me to learn more healthy ways of relating to another person.

Once I got used to the idea, the money seemed a small price to pay for the help I was getting from Dr Read; it was certainly cheaper than the emotional fee demanded in almost all of my other relationships. Six months after separating from Peter I dared to look toward the future. Ahead of me stretched a long road on which I was now taking the first few tentative steps. I felt that by moving forwards, however slowly, I might eventually learn how to take control of my life, and possibly even to help and understand my son. In the short term I was coping, and I did have some freedom. Peter baby-sat regularly, and occasionally even had Sam to stay overnight with him. Perhaps there were possibilities after all.

Then a bombshell struck – Peter was leaving Yorkshire. He was not moving just down the road either, but a very long way away. He would visit Sam once a month. No more going out, no more having someone to fall back upon, no more money – apart from an agreed contribution towards Sam's support. Life had altered considerably in the last six months but it was about to change even more. Now Sam and I would really have to manage on our own.

9

NEW DIRECTIONS

At least now my depression had lifted and so I was able to think more clearly about my problems. The first thing to think about was money. I needed an income, and so would have to find work as soon as possible. This would mean employing somebody to look after Sam between the time he finished school and when I was able to get home. Fortunately I found a job with my old firm, but the idea of working full-time as well as caring for Sam was daunting. As my first day back drew closer I worried about many things – my ability to do a job after so long, whether my colleagues would gossip about me (for they had all known Peter and me as a couple), and how Sam would cope. He would have to get used to being with somebody new and to seeing much less of me.

I did feel nervous, but was also excited about the prospect of escaping from domesticity and going back into the real world. I hoped I might manage better than I had in the past. I had never enjoyed my working life before, having always been so unsure of myself that other people terrified me. I was afraid to look anybody in the face, and this affected my ability to do my job properly. Now I had greater emotional resources and Dr Read to help me. Although apprehensive, I was looking forward with some curiosity to testing myself out.

Getting a job had been fairly easy but finding a childminder proved more difficult. I had hoped that one of the advantages of living in our new neighbourhood might be the likelihood of finding someone nearby to look after Sam. But now that did not seem possible. Caring for Sam was a full-time job, even if it was only for a couple of hours, and my neighbours all had their own children. I put an advertisement in the local paper. Everybody who applied either seemed to be unable to manage that time of day or else was intimidated by the idea of an autistic child. The hours were difficult, the child was difficult and the pay was not very good. I was just beginning to panic, when along came Lucy.

Lucy had worked with both disturbed and handicapped children. She was middle-aged yet single, and so able to work the awkward hours that I asked of her. She was a godsend. She came to our house for 3.30 p.m. when Sam arrived home from school. It felt strange leaving him in the care of somebody else. Apart from school, which seemed different because it was an official establishment, and the odd few hours he spent with his father or grandmother, Sam had never been away from me.

When he got home from school Lucy would chat to him, then cook his evening meal. She was calm and even-tempered – very different from Peter and myself, and just what Sam needed.

For the first month or two I felt so guilty about not being there for Sam that I spent every evening cooking to leave a ready-prepared dinner for his evening meal the following day. Eventually Lucy suggested that this was not really necessary. She was right. Sam was just as happy with the vegetables and hamburger that she cooked from the freezer. Lucy was thoroughly capable – good fortune had sent her my way. She had her quirks but then so did I. She made it possible for me to go out to work and the job suited her particular needs, so we both had a vested interest in making a success of our partnership. We soon fell into a routine.

When I got home Lucy would tell me how Sam had been – whether he had eaten his dinner and so on. Sam did not talk at all, so from him there was no feedback. After Lucy had gone I would try to establish some sort of communication with Sam, but seldom managed to do so. He would not look at me, and often ran to the farthest corner of the house in what appeared to be an effort to escape from me. This was hurtful. The effort required to pursue him was tremendous – I wanted nothing more than to obliterate the pain of his rejection by burying myself in a book.

Sam's holding-therapy sessions now had to be fitted in during the evening. Jennifer stressed the importance of this daily session – she said it would help maintain the bond between us now that we were apart for so much of the day. The thought of it hung over me like a lead weight from the minute I finished work. When I got home I would lie on the bed with Sam, holding his arms tightly and trying to force him to meet my gaze. We both longed to escape, but in my imagination Jennifer's face hovered above me. 'You must continue with the holding, Sam will be damaged even more if you stop. You must break through the barrier. You must force him to shout, for his own sake.' I kept trying – sometimes for an hour – but it was hopeless. We were both rigid with tension. The link between us was tenuous enough at the best of times. At this time of day when we had been apart for twenty-four hours, except for a brief half-hour in the morning, it was almost non-existent.

I do not believe that you can force closeness – the very words contradict each other. Closeness requires enough trust in the environment to allow relaxation and a lowering of defences. Forcefulness presents a challenge, and to someone as vulnerable as an autistic child – a threat. Whether or not the holding-therapy sessions in Jennifer's room had been helpful, these evening stints were destructive. I felt as though we were each encased in a cast-iron skin, and my attempts to blast a way through Sam's protective covering simply increased its strength. Several months later I more or less gave up trying to do this evening session with Sam, even at the risk of bringing Jennifer's wrath down upon me. I decided not to tell her that we had stopped doing holding therapy in the evenings, for I felt – rightly or wrongly – that she would be angry.

Instead of pushing for eye contact I sometimes sat Sam upon my knee and hoped he might just listen as I talked about what I thought might have happened during his day. Occasionally he did so, but most often he either got down immediately or behaved in a manic sort of way, laughing hysterically and throwing himself about. This made him as unreachable as the glassy stare or obsessive activities that he used to isolate himself at other times.

I soon found I dreaded going home in the evenings. This was not so on Fridays, for then the weekend stretched ahead, allowing enough time for Sam and me to re-establish our relationship and cocoon ourselves in our safe little world. The weekday evenings presented the conflict. At home I felt such a failure, frustrated by the feeling of not being able to either help or please Sam despite all my efforts to do so. Work on the other hand now seemed a friendly place and I was enjoying being back there.

Although my job was not terribly interesting the place and the social contact were stimulating. To my astonishment, people seemed to like me. How different they appeared from the Hogarthian characters I used to feel sneered and laughed at me when I had worked amongst them six years before. My view then had been distorted, but now things were falling into place. I was liked, I was welcomed – by these people at least, if not by Sam. Driving home over the moors I often thought about Sam and the way he controlled me. It reminded me of how my mother controlled every move I made when I was a child. Life seemed so unfair. At this time I really resented Sam. He pushed me away constantly, yet although he did not seem to want me himself he prevented me from forming other relationships which could prove more gratifying. Sam would not tolerate me talking to anyone for more than a minute or two, and so asking people to the house during the day was pointless. Evenings were even worse.

Sam was terrified of being left alone. Until the age of two he had gone to bed by himself, but for the past four years he had not been able to fall asleep on his own. If I went to go downstairs he simply ran after me. Nothing would persuade him to stay in his bedroom, and after the attempt at locking his door which had proved so disastrous all those years ago, I had not tried that again. I used to sit next to his bed or lie on my bed waiting, waiting. Occasionally he would drop off after half an hour or so, but usually it took much longer. It seems absurd now when I remember how I allowed Sam to dictate to me. He could not even bear for me to read whilst I sat – any move to do so would cause an outbreak of furious teeth-grinding. That waiting was a nightmare, and once I started working it began to seem intolerable. So long as Sam and I had remained isolated I had accepted this bedtime routine as a part of our strange, interdependent relationship. It all added up to the price I had to pay for not protecting him from the traumatic emotional events that had befallen him. But being in contact with the real world had shown me how ridiculous it was. I was spending fourteen hours a week just lying, feeling furious, doing nothing.

My only respite from this nightly ordeal was when Lucy baby-sat for me one evening a week. The first time she did this was not a success. I spent most of the evening upstairs seething; Lucy sat downstairs waiting for me to go out. When I did eventually come down at about 10.30 p.m., she had gone. I was horrified, but it made me realize that Lucy thought I was mad in allowing myself to be so manipulated. I supposed she had felt she was wasting her time. The next week she offered to sit with Sam herself. That evening and the following week she stayed by his bed knitting, the week after that she knitted in the room next door – from where Sam could still hear the clacking of her needles. Within a month Lucy was able to put him to bed then go down and spend the evening watching television. He went to sleep on his own, within half an hour. I was astonished. 'Right,' I thought. 'Right. If you can do it for her you can do it for me.' But he didn't. So we then had a situation where for one evening in the week Sam went off easily and without fuss. For the rest of the week the nightmare continued.

I looked forward to my night out all week but between it and me were my two hours at home with Sam. These two hours were often an ordeal. Sam would have had his meal so I would whisk him upstairs, bath him, then take him into my room and attempt to do his therapy. He resisted strongly. He knew I was going out and resented the fact; I knew he knew and felt guilty about it. His tension often manifested itself in a barrage of clicking noises. How uncomfortable I was, knowing Lucy was sitting downstairs, a witness to my hopeless attempts to relax my son. Quite unreasonably I resented her presence in the house even though I was grateful to her for baby-sitting. When it was time for me to go Sam always stayed happily with Lucy, who then put him to bed without any bother. I would feel a rush of freedom as I drove away. I often stayed out very late. Sometimes when I got home and went to bed Sam would wake up.

He is driving me mad at the moment, continually sitting up as I write this. He sits bolt upright for a second or two then lies down again. This has been going on for weeks. I feel as though he manipulates me into interacting with him. Out of the corner of my eye I can see his shadow on the wall, but I'm trying not to turn and look, or to acknowledge what he is doing. If I do I'll be drawn into something that could go on for hours.

Lucy's success in getting Sam to bed made me understand that her method of achieving her aim via several intermediate stages was the way I too should set about cracking the bedtime problem. It was going to take me a lot longer than it had taken her, though. At first I sat just outside his door.

I've been sitting outside Sam's room for the last two hours. Tonight for the first time he actually fell asleep on his own in his own room! He is six years old and it is quarter past eleven.

Several weeks later I moved slightly further away from the door so that my body was hidden from view but my feet were just visible. Sam needed the guarantee of being able to see me. It was cold and uncomfortable sitting there but there was one great advantage – now I could read. This had not seemed possible when I lay beside Sam on the bed. He did not like me reading, and thinking was also out of the question. I was always so anxiously attuned to his every movement that my mind had seemed not to belong to me. We were hypersensitive to each other, and responded to each other's slightest gesture. I sometimes felt we were two warring factions of the same person.

A book I had read recently caused me to recall that feeling vividly. *The Silent Twins* by Marjorie Wallace is about twin autistic girls. During their childhood and adolescence the girls were left very much to their own devices. Communication between them and the outside world was limited and somewhat odd but the relationship that existed between the twins themselves was intense. They also were hypersensitive to each other in every aspect, to the extent that it was suggested that they communicated by ESP. I understood the nature of this introspective, self-contained relationship. As with Sam and me, these two girls focused obsessively upon each other. They were like two spotlights, each burning fiercely into the other while all else remained in darkness. I'm sure they also were finely attuned to each other's body language, facial expression and subtle mood variations in the same way that Sam and I were.

It has been suggested that their twinship somehow caused the psychological interdependence of these two girls. Spending so

As a baby, Sam responded to faces and objects like any other infant.

Left: *Sam's fear of a step reveals an autistic apprehension of distance.*

Below: *Although displaying certain autistic traits, Sam demonstrates here a clear ability to interact with his father.*

Right: *At an early age Sam developed avoidance techniques – a typical sign of autism – such as turning his face away from direct contact.*

Below: *His delight in blowing bubbles revealed his ability to play normal childhood games.*

As *Sam grew older he developed the autistic habit of clutching an ob* *obsessively. This helicopter was one of his favourites.*

Although we had problems, sometimes the three of us could look an *behave like a perfectly 'normal' family.*

A day at the fair, soon after Peter and I had separated. Sam had a lovely time, and it made me wish that we were all together again.

Sam's attitude to animals was ambivalent. Usually he was petrified of them, but he felt at ease on horseback, and was captivated by a friendly cow.

Above: *The whole school was invited to Sam's birthday party, but he found it difficult to cope with so many people.*

Left & below: *One of Sam's few real friends was Tim, with whom he loved to play rough-and-tumble games.*

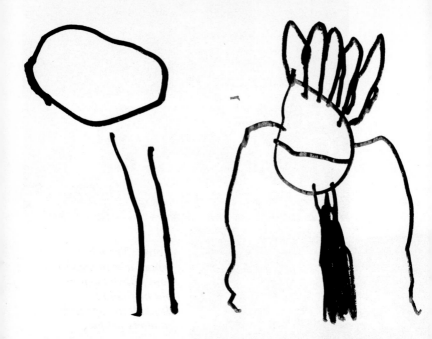

These drawings span a period of four years and show, I think, the
progression of Sam's view of people as he developed a sense of his ou
identity.

much time locked away together did enable them to evolve and maintain the fantasy world in which they both lived, untempered by adult or outside influence, but the autistic withdrawal must surely have preceded the obsessive relationship that developed between them. It may have been not that their 'strange secret bondage' caused them to reject the outside world, but that their individual rejection of the world fostered their strange secret bondage. Neither of the girls seemed to relate to their mother. Perhaps the relationship was damaged early in life, and each twin tried to extract from the other what she had failed to get from her mother. Many a description by one of the girls of sitting, watching, waiting for a sign from the other, being controlled and sometimes feeling annihiliated by the other, rang true for me and I'm sure also for Sam.

We were still tied together by a very short rope – I was after all only just outside his bedroom – but the fact that we could not see one another made things easier. Without the visual aspect to our interaction I could to some extent distance myself from Sam, or at least avoid responding to his every movement.

It is five to ten and Sam has just dropped off, which is unusually early. I've been sitting in this chair where Lucy sits, reading. He could see my feet on the banister when he sat up to check but I could not see him which is good as there is less temptation to say anything or get angry. I controlled the urge to tell him to lie down when I thought he was sitting up at one point. I spoke only twice when I thought he was getting out of bed. I'm pleased with the result.

This stage continued for many months. My every attempt to withdraw completely from Sam's view caused him to leap out of bed to check that I was still there. And so I continued reading – mostly books about psychology.

One book was *The Riddle of Autism*. The author, George Victor, makes a thorough study of autism in all its aspects, from a consideration of the autistic-like individuals described in myths and literary works to an account of how the condition develops. This broad but integrating perspective analyses a wide diversity of material, from laboratory experiments with animals to parents' accounts of their autistic children. George Victor plots a course through events and the responses to them which can result in autism.

He starts before the child is born and finishes with an ingenious analogy illustrating autistic development. He suggests that the combination of reasons for autism occurring may be thought of as a railway. A train may be boarded at any point during infancy or early childhood as a means of escaping from what is perceived by the child as an intolerably stressful situation. If a person gets on after those first few formative years it is likely that enough normal development will have occurred to preclude autistic withdrawal. Problems occurring later would cause a stress reaction that was less severe than autism. At first the train stops frequently so people can get on or off. The stops represent opportunities – such as a reduction in stress or a change in circumstances – for a potentially autistic child to get back on the path of normal development. But as time goes by the train gathers speed and stops become less frequent. The branch lines, representing the different autistic behaviours and strategies, merge into the main line and the train becomes an express. The final destination – autism – is the same for all, regardless of why their development began to deviate from normal, or how this difference manifested itself initially.

When I first read this book I skimmed through some sections very quickly, partly because there was so much to assimilate but mostly because what I read was so painful. The descriptions of mothers of autistic children struck me particularly – how they often conformed to a type and usually suffered from depression. How such mothers had contradictory impulses towards their children, resenting their presence yet needing them desperately, often counting on them to fulfil unrealistic expectations.

I had certainly been depressed, and looking back I could see how my unborn child had represented for me a possible escape route from my unhappy state of mind. I remembered how I used to sit alone in the woods when I was pregnant. I had a secluded spot from which the tree-covered slope fell away below me, so that I looked down into the branches. I loved the rustling of the leaves – beneath them I used to sit and dream, imagining how my child and I would play together in the woods secretly, as I had done when I was young. I liked to think of how we would create a world of our own that no one else could enter or spoil. Being alone had always seemed safer to me than being with other people, and perhaps I hoped that my baby would cure the results of my own upbringing by filling the holes in my life. But then I did not know what I was doing, or expecting, and sailed forth in blissful ignorance of what lay ahead.

Reading George Victor's book, I began to see how great a part parental inconsistency played in the development of autism. One of the things that he discusses in detail is the way ambiguous behaviour and contradictory cues given by parents can have a devastating effect on their children's development. A child has no yardstick by which to gauge the relevance of his actions other than the response which such actions evoke from the people around him. If the same behaviour evokes different responses at different times from his parents, the child is denied the fundamental experience of cause and effect.

Experiments with animals illustrate this principle well. The rat experiment interested me particularly. Rats were trained to perform a series of actions that resulted either in the appearance of food or in the rat receiving a blow on his nose. At one point in the sequence, rats had to decide between two doors. They quickly learned which door to opt for in order to get food. When the identifying marks on the doors were switched, the rats seemed confused and resisted making a choice between the doors. They were coerced into doing so. The rats became disturbed. When the cues were switched again and the rats were again forced to make a choice, they became more disturbed. Then the task was made impossible by placing food behind the doors in a random manner. The rats manifested their now serious disturbance by squealing when touched, refusing altogether to eat, chattering, urinating and defecating excessively during training sessions. Subsequently most rats adopted a new pattern of behaviour – a fixed habit. For example, the rats continually attempted to open the same door, regardless of its identifying marks or whether they found food behind it or not. Their behaviour seemed purposeless. The rats had ceased responding to environmental stimuli and had become locked into a rigid pattern of behaviour in an attempt to create order in an impossibly unpredictable situation.

George Victor sees adoption of rituals, isolation and lack of communication all as adaptations to the initial unreliability of parents or other caretakers experienced by the infant at a time of total vulnerability. For children whose mothers alternate between involvement and withdrawal, life must seem precarious. Slow-motion analysis of mothers and babies has revealed an elaborate synchronization between their actions and responses to each other. The way that a mother behaves with her child is to a great extent governed by her own past experience: the way that the child behaves is largely determined by how his mother treats him. If he does not receive food in response to his cry, words in acknowledgement of his vocalizations, or a smile to meet his gaze, then he has nothing. A child cannot rationalize about why he has not been responded to, or defer his needs until later. He needs feedback from his mother to reinforce his actions. These reinforcements enhance his sense of self, and without them the child lacks the motivation to progress in his development.

George Victor explains how lack of predictability is traumatic for members of a number of species. As the rat experiment shows, random responses are even more disorientating than no responses at all. In such a situation a child feels powerless, and at the mercy of forces beyond his control or understanding.

Now I could see how such ambivalence could lead to severe disturbance. Reading back through my diary I could also see how my handling of Sam was chaotic, although it had never occurred to me at the time.

Since the recent bedtime fiasco I've decided to try getting Sam to bed on his own. Wednesday, Friday and Saturday I kept telling him to go gack to bed when he got up. Thursday he slept on the sofa, also Sunday and Monday as we were out late those nights. So far he will at least keep going back when I tell him to, and does not seem frightened. He does keep coming down the stairs though, which is infuriating. If I think he is in a tense state I avoid the issue and let him fall asleep on the sofa.

Learning about the autistic condition through reading *The Riddle of Autism* was fascinating. Although such terms as non-contingent reinforcement, negativism and altered consciousness meant noth-ing to me then, much of what I read was a direct reflection of my own experiences with Sam. Alimentary disturbances, sleep problems, allergies, obsession with bright lights, masturbation, staring at objects – all of these things were or had at some time been a part of our lives.

New but more interesting was the idea that when they are not indulging in obsessional or self-stimulating activities autistic children are hypersensitive to the behaviour of people around them. This is not apparent, because they keep strict control over their emotions. These they dampen, restrain or deny, displacing feelings on to insignificant events or meaningless activities. But although these children avoid eye contact, they do still look at people. They use peripheral vision a great deal; I recalled Sam's darting, sidelong glances. As he grew older I assumed that he had stopped doing this, but perhaps he had simply refined his technique.

Autistic children also rely on clues such as their parents' perspiration, skin temperature, muscle tension and tiny involuntary movements. These cues, George Victor says, they have learned from experience to be more reliable indications of the real attitudes and expectations of their parents, whose behaviour and words often send conflicting messages. For example a mother may express love and concern for her child verbally, yet her tone and manner will state quite clearly that she feels angry. By attending more to the person herself than to what she is saying or trying to show him, the child gleans hidden yet more reliable information.

What I read made sense to me. Quite apart from the inconsistencies in my behaviour, I could see that there was an enormous difference between the way I attempted to behave and the way I really felt. I was tense and anxious much of the time, trying to maintain control over the precarious circumstances in which we lived. Sam must have sensed that I was angry, frightened and insecure, despite my attempts to be even-tempered and reliable. I am sure I took things out on him – there was no one else.

Jennifer tried to help the relationship by telling me that I should resent the extreme demands that Sam made upon me. Both she and Martha Welch seemed to believe that autistic behaviour was to some extent perverse – that autistic children chose to behave abnormally and could act differently if they so wished. They felt I should tell Sam how angry I was that he had spoiled my life. This worried me. At the time I accepted what they said, but on later reflection it seemed clear that far from spoiling my life, Sam was a product of the spoiling that had occurred long before he came along. Although it was not my fault I reacted as I did towards him, it certainly was not his fault either, and I after all had far greater resources to deal with our difficult relationship.

Several months later Martha Welch came to stay with Jennifer for a short visit. Martha knew all about our 'case' even though we had never met until the Saturday when she came along to our session in the holding-therapy room. I felt that I was in the presence of the possessor of ultimate knowledge as we sat drinking coffee together, for Martha Welch was the guru of our little group.

Met Martha on Saturday. She says Sam could talk. She says he could do normal things for his age, and that everything depends upon my expectations of him. He cannot learn to do what I do not expect of him. I must insist upon a response, upon speech and normal behaviour. She says I must get very angry with him for the things he does to me and the extreme demands he makes, and that I should say so to him. When he does something outrageous (she thought most of his behaviour was outrageous) I should make it clear that it was intolerable. Shout 'Stop it', for example.

Peter was with us on this occasion and Martha had plenty of advice for all of us. But while in itself it was probably sensible, like so much good advice it did not take account of what our actual problems were, and how we could get from the situation we were in to where we wanted to be. The new insight Martha had seemed to offer disappeared as quickly as the rainbow we followed for the first few miles of our homeward journey.

Since Peter had left Yorkshire Sam was obviously seeing much less of him. Although this now meant I had total responsibility for Sam, I could see how the new arrangement was better for all of us. Although Peter and I were still tied to each other in many respects, we did now have our own lives. We saw each other only once a month when he came to stay at the house, ostensibly to visit Sam. These weekends alternated between good and bad.

I remember one lovely day we spent at a leisure park. We

played about in boats on the lake, rode the water chute and the carousel, ate and drank and took endless photographs. We must have looked like any other nuclear family – how I wished that we were. Why on earth could we not make it work, I wondered.

As always when relations were happy between Peter and myself, Sam was delighted at having us together, and I could see the advantages for him of having his father around. Although I was more consistent (which is not to say very) than Peter, he added a different and perhaps more exciting element to our outings. He did things with Sam that I would never do – like sending him down the fifty-foot slide and sitting him on a motorbike, which Sam loved. Sam had a wonderful day. He had never before shown any interest in farm animals but on this occasion became deeply enamoured of the cows when we visited the leisure park's model farmyard. He offered his tiny tractor to several of them – a truly magnanimous gesture on his part that was barely even acknowledged by the ungrateful beasts. He touched their noses gingerly with a delicate finger, squirming with pleasure at his bravado as he did so. Sam was a delight in this mood – a tentative self unfurling like a tiny new leaf. No doubt he was responding to the relaxed atmosphere, sadly destined not to last. Peter got angry as I drove us home. Sam ground his teeth, I sank into depression.

Although parting at the end of a visit was still painful for all of us, I was beginning to appreciate the calm that returned to our household when Peter left. Getting through one of his visits was like crossing a choppy sea in a small boat.

With less emotional clutter to consume my energy I found myself better able to plan things in my life. I decided I could no longer stand sleeping in the same bedroom with Sam, for he and I were still in adjacent beds. I spent some time considering ways of changing this before settling on what proved to be a good idea. I had bought Sam a large trampoline for Christmas – it was almost exactly the same size as my double bed. He loved bouncing up and down upon it, no doubt appreciating the chance to release some of his pent-up energy. The trampoline was in a somewhat inaccessible part of the house; my plan involved explaining to Sam that he could have it in his room but that I would have to move my bed out to make the space. He accepted the idea with surprisingly good grace – perhaps he wanted me out of his room anyway.

My own room was decorated and waiting for me. I remember the first night that I slept there. Freedom is relative, of course, but for me at that time just sleeping in a room on my own felt like freedom. In fact it was bliss. I would lie awake reading, moving about without fear of waking Sam and positively enjoying the heavenly silence that descended in the absence of his snuffles.

10

NEW SCHOOL

My most pressing worry at the beginning of Sam's sixth year was the need to sort out his schooling. There just didn't seem to be anywhere for him to go. In some ways I was grateful he had been allowed to stay so long where he was – he had now been three years in what was theoretically an assessment unit. As long as he remained uncategorized there was hope that he might improve and avoid the 'seriously retarded' label, but at the same time I wanted him settled in a place where I knew he could stay.

His teacher and I had long disagreed about both the nature and cause of Sam's condition and about his developmental potential. Mrs Stanley did not believe the reasons for his retardation to be particularly important anyway; she pointed out that the child we had to deal with was the same regardless of past events or labels. I felt that while this was true theoretically, in practice people's behaviour is tailored specifically to fit the person they think they are dealing with. With Sam it was extremely difficult to assess who this person was or how much he did actually understand. He was practically mute; so speech gave no clue. He had poor concentration and apparently little motivation to acquire skills, and was often too apathetic to attempt what was asked of him. If his potential was gauged by his performance Sam scored very badly. His verbal abilities belied his level of comprehension. To assume that Sam understood as little as his restricted speech seemed to indicate would inevitably limit the way one talked to him, and so deny him the input he so badly needed.

The emotional aspect of a situation was everything to Sam. His area of interest did not extend far beyond himself and his immediate surroundings, but within these parameters his perception and understanding were acute. Yet if the way was not made smooth for him he did not cope. If Sam was treated in a way that did not take his sensitivities into account he simply cut himself off psychologically by ceasing to look, listen or respond. Then it was utterly pointless trying to do anything with him. For this reason I felt that understanding why Sam behaved to strangely would not only give everyone a more accurate picture of him as a person, but would provide his teachers with a more powerful tool for effecting change than simply training him to behave differently.

From time to time I chipped in with my interpretations of events, but quite often I felt in the dark as to what was actually going on at school. At some point it was decided that Sam should see a certain teacher in a separate classroom for a short period several times a week to do pencil work. Apparently Sam did not take to her – and neither did I when we met. She told me I was deluding myself about my son, that he understood very little of what was said to him and that he would never amount to anything much. My best bet, she advised, would be to put him into a school for severely retarded children, and to turn my mind to other things. Quite apart from the fact that what she said nearly broke my heart, I was horrified that this teacher should voice such opinions in front of Sam, who certainly did understand what she said. Sam did not go for his 'special sessions' with her again, and the need to find him a new school became even more pressing. It seemed impossible. I had already visited two suggested schools and found them to be unsuitable. A third I had dismissed because it was too far away and too big; and because they used behaviour modification techniques that seemed to me quite inappropriate for autistic children.

Driving home from a friend's house one day I noticed a large rambling Victorian building set well back from the road, almost hidden from view by the surrounding trees. My friend said she thought it was some sort of school, which prompted me to make enquiries. In fact it turned out to be a special school. When I eventually got through to the headmaster I liked him immediately. We arranged for me to call and see him. By the time of my visit I had found out only that Springfield was a school for disturbed children, that it took weekly boarders as well as day pupils, and that for some reason its numbers were down.

The education department of the local council seemed unaware of the school's existence, which surprised me, since they nominally ran it. Mrs Stanley thought it was for socially deprived children and quite unsuitable for Sam. Another source informed me that Springfield had closed two years earlier. I arrived at the front door with some trepidation, but was pleasantly surprised by what I found. The nodding daffodils and the smell of freshly baked biscuits boded well as far as I was concerned. The clutter of child-produced artefacts in the headmaster's office spoke volumes. Also the tone of the notices pinned up here and there appealed to me – 'Children must *not* [heavily underlined] be punished for bedwetting.' I liked this school.

I spent several hours talking with the headmaster and left feeling optimistic. I was impressed by his attitude, his compassion and his obvious sympathy with the problems of some of his young charges. I liked the firm but caring structure that was apparent in the school, which was somehow complemented by a lightness of touch and a sense of joyful involvement shared by staff and children.

Quite apart from the atmosphere, the building itself was beautiful. Although I knew this was irrelevant as far as Sam's education was concerned, it somehow mattered to me. The lovely old place had previously been a nursing home, and stood in secluded isolation about ten miles from the nearest town, yet only three or four miles from where we lived. Much more important for Sam was that it was very close to the airport, so he could watch the aeroplanes taking off and landing just two fields away.

The fact that the school housed far fewer children than it was able to accommodate bothered me slightly, for I could not understand why children were not being referred to such a marvellous establishment. There were several children in Sam's class at the assessment unit, for example, who would have benefited from such a placement. Not until much later, when the local authority tried to close Springfield because of its low numbers, did the reason for lack of referrals become apparent.

Because there were so few children – there were only seventeen at that time – the school's resources were limited. Their main asset was plenty of space, both in and outside the building, but there was less teaching equipment, fewer visiting professionals, and less money available here than at Sam's present school. I wondered whether Sam might not miss out in some ways if he came to Springfield – I was always worried about him being 'deprived'. There was just a chance that he might be accepted into the first class of the school that housed his assessment unit and for months I agonized over the choice between pushing for this and trying for a place at Springfield. Eventually I opted for the latter, which looking back I think was quite brave of me. Not only was it against the advice of staff in his present school, but the low numbers at Springfield seemed to indicate that few parents wanted their children to go there. Despite contra-indications I followed my instinctive feeling that this would be a good place for Sam, and I never had cause to regret it.

Arrangements were made for Sam to begin at Springfield after the summer holiday, which meant he had one more term in the assessment unit. Things were not going well there for him. One afternoon I got a letter from Mrs Stanley saying that he had had a tantrum at school – unusual for Sam. Although his behaviour was sometimes peculiar, difficult to handle, or disruptive, he rarely gave full vent to his emotions. I often wished that he would do so. An angry child is at least a living child. Mrs Stanley described in her letter how Sam had lost control completely – thrown chairs, emptied bins, swept toys to the floor. No one seemed to have any idea why he was so angry, or to consider that he had any right to be so. Mrs Stanley was obviously furious. She showed her anger by punishing Sam – he was smacked and sent to sit alone, and told he was naughty and not wanted by the group. It distressed me to think how confused and resentful this must have made him feel. In the holding-therapy sessions he was urged to express his emotions and berated by Jennifer for not doing so, yet when on this one occasion at school he was unable to maintain his iron grip and his feelings did slip out of control he was punished. There was nothing to be done. I had not been present and so did not know what had really happened. Sam could tell me nothing. It seemed that the school term would never end, but at last it did. I photographed Sam's classmates, his teachers, his classroom, so that for better or for worse he would have a visual record of the time he had spent amongst them.

We had always taken photographs of Sam, and once they had been stuck into albums he began to take great interest in them. When he first started looking at the albums – when he was about five – he did so only in private. If anyone entered the room when Sam was browsing he would feign lack of interest, and drift away. I never interfered, and his self-consciousness (if that was what it was) soon wore off. Then he was often to be found poring over certain photographs or flicking through the pages, searching frantically for a particular image that he obviously held in his memory. Sometimes there were clear connections – for example if I told him that somebody was coming to visit he would rush off to look up that person's photograph – but on many occasions I could not decipher the links he seemed to make. He once, for no apparent reason, became wildly excited about a picture of himself aged two sitting in his sandpit. I was mystified until I noticed that a tiny toy car he had recently resurrected from the cellar was lying there in the sandpit, almost entirely obscured. Sam was experiencing once again the joy of uniting like with like.

Sam's first day at Springfield was not the calm and happy event I had hoped for. Perhaps I imagined that the staff would be lined up outside waiting to receive us, arms outstretched in greeting. A ship sailing into a welcoming harbour, a thousand hands waiting to help the passengers ashore. I had taken pains to explain that Sam would be terrified and insecure in this new environment (at least I thought I had but perhaps I forgot to mention it) and was horrified by the jumble of children and bags and clothes that met our arrival at school. Every child I came across seemed to want or need something – the staff were not to be found. No doubt the fact that Springfield was a boarding school contributed to the general upheaval of the 'first day back'. Eventually someone did come to take Sam and I left for work feeling anxious and fearful on his behalf.

Springfield was so different from the claustrophobic yet safe unit in which Sam had spent the last three years. For one thing the scale of the building and the distances were so much greater, for another his day would be broken up into several classes and he would have to move from one room to another. It may be difficult to imagine why this seemed a problem, but I knew just how Sam would feel about it. His world was tiny – he needed it to be so – and in the assessment unit he could see all four walls at once. His environment did not alter; he knew exactly what was happening, and when. At Springfield things were constantly changing, people came and went, every day was different. I did not think that Sam would cope, but he did.

Once again I was grateful for Lucy's presence – she was a bridge that spanned Sam's past and present experience of school. For almost a year she had been there waiting at the front door for him when he got home each afternoon, and now that he had been catapulted into this new situation she was still there. She was constant and reliable, and she almost always stayed unruffled when dealing with Sam. She expected him to behave 'sensibly', as she put it, and he usually did when he was with her. Lucy and Sam both enjoyed walking, and sometimes after school or during holidays they would go on long rambles together into the countryside. She also took him to swings and parks, and did not seem to be anxious or self-conscious with him in the way that I was.

I was very pleased to have got Sam into Springfield, for in our part of the country at least it was unusual for a child as handicapped as he was to be admitted into a school for children with psychological/emotional problems. Autism is viewed by many educationalists in this country as a physiological impairment even though this remains unproved and the impairment unidentifiable. Autistic children are not expected to recover. This put Sam into a different category from his fellow pupils, who would, it was hoped, learn to function and progress normally. They all had behavioural and related learning difficulties, some of them quite severe – but the problems were more obviously linked to their disturbed backgrounds.

Although at seven years of age Sam looked relatively normal – apart from his detached air and his anxious physical postures – there could be no doubt that in terms of functioning he was severely retarded. It was only because I had found the school myself and done my own negotiations, and because Springfield was short of children, that he had managed to slip in under the 'emotionally disturbed' umbrella. His classmates were all far more able than he was. They were all speaking, and some would soon go back into mainstream education.

When Sam arrived at Springfield he had already been statemented. This Statement of Special Educational Needs is the official document that aims to identify and assess the needs of a handicapped child. It presented the official view of my son. Although I did not completely agree with what was said, I knew it was important for me to see how Sam fitted into this broader context, and how he appeared to an objective observer.

Below are some sections from Sam's statement, most of which would have been written when he was between five and six years of age:

Cognitive Skills

Sam can match objects and put them into simple categories and has developed concepts of one-to-one correspondence. He can complete and sequence appropriately and can do simple six-piece jigsaw puzzles. He knows most body parts and can differentiate between a boy and a girl.

However, he cannot count or use any descriptive language to recall events. Memory appears to be good and he can indicate which of three objects has been removed. He knows some colours and can indicate appropriately when requested, but he cannot name them. Pencil control is not well developed. Generally, therefore, I would estimate his functioning at around the three-to-four-year level.

Motor Skills

Gross motor skills are fairly well developed and Sam can walk up and down stairs and can run well, although with a somewhat unco-ordinated appearance. Fine motor skills are perhaps less well developed and although Sam can put pieces in a formboard he cannot yet roll platicine into a ball or use a pencil.

Language Skills

Sam's language is not well developed. He will rarely use speech, and this is usually limited to single words of one syllable. Occasionally a word may be used in completion of a given sentence, e.g., 'you sweep with a . . .' Sam, however, prefers to use gestures and eye-pointing to make his needs known and, therefore, given that his speech production is also immature, the use of a sign-system may be indicated.

Receptive language appears somewhat better and Sam can understand instructions and requests, but this appears limited to around the two to two-and-a-half-year level.

Social and Self-Help Skills
These are reasonably good. Sam can feed himself with a spoon and fork but needs food cut up for him. He still requires help with dressing and supervision when using the toilet. Social skills are around the two-year level and co-operative play does not yet appear to have developed.

Elsewhere in the statement I came across some observations with which I could not agree. There were, for example, descriptions of Sam's strengths and weaknesses. It astonished me to learn that he 'enjoyed learning and always worked well in a one-to-one situation'. I would have said he had a massive learning block. And that his 'relationship and eye contact with adults is good'. Good compared with what? Certainly not with a normal child. He still rarely looked directly at other people and does not do so even now, years later. Most amazing of all, however, was the claim that 'many of the signs of his autism have largely diminished or disappeared in the last two years, e.g., lack of eye contact and disinterest in people, repetitive play patterns'. This observation seemed to be contradicted even within the same document, where in the description of Sam's weaknesses the following appeared:

> Sam shows anxiety in new situations; he becomes tense and grinds his teeth and bites his sleeve. It needs great persistence to get his attention in the group . . . His play is solitary, alongside others. He never plays with another child and rarely shows any interest in them. Shows great insecurity if left even for a moment.

It had always seemed to me that at Sam's first school there was some sort of desire to prove that he was not autistic. I never understood why, and I have since met other parents who have suffered from this same treatment. Even though his autism could not be denied – he had been diagnosed by a leading specialist in the field – his autistic symptoms were said to have 'disappeared' while he was at the school. I only wish they had. There can be no handicap more crippling than this devastating affliction that divides these children from the rest of their kind, leaving them stranded in a lonely asocial world where they are cut off from love, life and learning. The first step in dealing with a problem must be to define what that problem is, and this is just what Sam's new teacher set out to do.

When Sam started at Springfield there were about eight children in the first class. Most of the time there were two staff – a teaching aid and the teacher, Mrs Thompson. Here we had struck good fortune. She was a marvellous teacher – sensitive, intelligent, and intuitive. Although some of the other children at the school had 'autistic features' (communication or obsessional problems), Mrs Thompson had not taught a child as withdrawn as Sam before, and unlike the medical and educational professionals that we had previously encountered she seemed not to have a rigid set of preconceived ideas about his condition. In order to learn about Sam for herself she watched him closely, and she was perceptive.

Right from the start, she adopted a 'softly, softly' approach. She decided that at first she would allow Sam to get on with his own thing, which meant that for some months he spent a fair amount of time playing in the sandpit. Sam did not actually 'play' in the accepted sense of the word – playing implies a determination, a will to manipulate the environment that he did not possess. He did dig a little sometimes, but castle-building and tunnel construction were beyond him. Mostly he just moved the sand about, or ran it through his fingers. It seemed that he chose the sandpit more because he wanted to be in it than for wanting to do anything in particular with its contents. Perhaps it provided a safe retreat from his new and overwhelming environment. Whatever the reason, Mrs Thompson felt it was important that Sam be allowed to settle at his new school in his own time. For many months he clung to the safety of his sandy world, but gradually Mrs Thompson began to ease him out.

She soon realized that Sam grasped at least some of what was said to him because he reacted appropriately to requests like, 'Pass me the spade, please.' Having concluded that he understood more than was at first apparent, she set out to establish his level of comprehension. She talked to him in the sandpit while he sifted, mostly about the pictures that she showed him – watching always for signs of interest or recognition. At this stage he looked very little at her but he did sometimes betray an interest in the pictures, especially if they were of cars, helicopters or aeroplanes. At these he looked intently. Mrs Thompson made a mental list of the things Sam seemed to like and used them as a basis for talking to him. Her method was to wait for him to show interest, then to expand upon it. She did not try to coerce him; she avoided types of approach that might cause him stress, feeling that this would be counterproductive. She knew he would cut off if pushed too far, and at this time very little would have been too far.

Yet all the time there was language all around Sam, for Mrs Thompson ran an activity-based classroom, and the children were encouraged to talk to each other. Although he did not join in, Sam watched and listened from a distance, returning to his sandpit for support or escape whenever he wanted.

As far as she could Mrs Thompson tailored her treatment of Sam to fit his needs. If she had not been genuinely interested in him she would not have learned to understand him as well as she did. Even so, Sam's enigmatic behaviour must have baffled her at times. Being so unlike those of normal people his signals were difficult to interpret, yet I always longed for others to see them for what they were – a cry for help. I usually felt that I could understand how Sam was feeling, but the frustrating thing was that because of my own anxiety I was often unable to help him. When he ground his teeth or made odd throaty noises, for example, my embarrassment would cause me to tense immediately. He did these things because he was himself anxious, but he would become even more so when he saw that I felt the same way.

One particular form of anxiety that developed about this time was Sam's aversion to (or fear of) other children. If he saw a child coming towards him in the street he would try to escape into a shop or pull me frantically into the road in his effort to avoid them. I had read that this fear sometimes appeared in autistic children when they started lowering their defences slightly as they felt more vulnerable as they came into closer contact with the real world – but that did not make it any easier to deal with.

Usually we could get away from this sort of situation, but escape was more difficult when we were on public view. I remember well the Christmas play at Sam's school. I sat in the front row of the audience – handy in case of an emergency. Sam was a snowdrop. How I prayed he would not do anything too silly. His appearance was a token one only. After a few minutes he was led down to sit with me, where I did my best to restrain him for the rest of the performance, in which he showed no interest whatsoever. He was so anxious – almost rigid with tension – yet despite my worry and concern for him my reassurances provided no comfort. I could not forge any supporting link between us.

Although Sam seemed oblivious when in the company of other children, he was not uninterested in them. This was apparent when he brought home his first school photograph, with which he became extremely preoccupied for many months. He would pull my hand towards the picture then place my forefinger on it so that I was pointing at one of the figures. Then he would gaze at my face, wanting me to name the person at whom I was pointing. Sam was not unable to recognize the people or remember their names. Both his perceptive abilities and his memory were very good. He just needed constant reaffirmation. It was as though he did not trust his own perceptions.

When Sam first started at Springfield Mrs Thompson feared that he might be picked upon by the other children, but in fact they tended to mother him. His social abilities were practically nil. Even when he did not adopt one of his 'cutting-off' mechanisms he gave nothing in return for any attempt to interact with him. His eye contact was minimal, and he would either turn away or look straight through whoever was speaking to him. Yet there was one little boy in particular who took to Sam. Although Tim had many problems of his own, he was undaunted by Sam's lack of responsiveness. He liked looking after him and telling him what to do, and gradually a link was forged between these two. It was based on mutual need, as I suppose are all human relationships. Tim needed someone who could receive his endless ministrations without becoming fed up, or bored, or telling him to go away. He lavished instruction and attention upon Sam, who responded with silent acquiescence. Perhaps he was pleased to have come across a child who did not give up on him. These two were thrown together by pure chance, but they seemed to have much to offer each other.

One day during Sam's first year at Springfield I was visiting school when I looked into the television room. To my astonishment he was on the floor with Tim, play-wrestling. I could hardly believe my eyes. I had never seen him do anything like that before. We had rough-and-tumble games sometimes, and occasionally he would instigate a game of 'come and catch me', but this was real interaction with a peer. It gave me tremendous pleasure to see him rolling about laughing with another child.

Slowly Sam's eye contact began to improve. A very slight thaw began to melt his icy detachment. He had been at Springfield for almost a year and a half before Mrs Thompson felt that he was starting to 'come out of his shell and look around a bit'. She had always felt that a secure relationship between herself and Sam was an essential basis from which to begin more structured learning, and she had succeeded in establishing this. Sam trusted her, but because he did he felt it was safe for him to set about testing her out. For months he pinched her hands with his fingers – she was covered in bruises – while scrutinizing her face for signs of a reaction. I was full of admiration for the way she handled this. She did not lose her temper or try to retaliate, she just told him 'No' and held his hands, or tried to interest him in something more constructive. She assumed that he would get through this phase, which he did.

In many ways Sam's behaviour became more difficult to handle as his interest in people became more overt. Then quite suddenly he started saying the word 'people' – and pointing at them. Sometimes he even allowed the drivers of his toy cars and tractors to remain in their seats instead of being hurled behind the sofa.

His observations of other children had always been surreptitious – now he began to show his interest, even though his methods were sometimes quite alarming. He went through a phase of running towards particular children and trying to grab their throats. Naturally they were horrified, although I think that Sam's extraordinary behaviour was more an expression of his uncontrollable excitement than any intention to hurt or harm them. He was thinking about other people and the possibility of relating to them, and such thoughts caused wild, uncontainable rushes of emotion.

Until Sam was about six years old he had always been asked to at least one birthday party a year – that of my friend Jo's son, Harry. One day I noticed that Harry's birthday had passed without trace. I was very upset. This rejection of Sam, as I saw it, made me feel utterly miserable. I could see what had happened of course. Harry was now at school and wanting to make his own friends rather than simply mixing with the children of his mother's acquaintances.

It frightened me to think of Sam as being so bereft of connections with other children. The obligation that I had always felt to provide him with a birthday party – though I had no way of knowing whether he wanted one or not – was becoming more difficult to fulfil. Who to invite? I asked Mrs Thompson whether there were any other children at the school apart from Tim who would like to come to Sam's party. She explained that as their numbers were so small at Springfield they tended to do things as a group. And so we asked them all.

The party was lovely – a chaos of sausages and jellies, and wine for the adults, for Mrs Thompson and several house-parents came too. Although I could not say that Sam thoroughly enjoyed himself, I'm sure that he appreciated the status of being the 'party person'. He blew out his candles and joined in pass-the-parcel – managing to cope for about an hour before cutting off and retreating into his private world. That was a long time for Sam, and I was delighted.

Springfield had provided us with a ready-made group of children, and it was proving to be helpful in other ways as well. Because it was a boarding school the concern of the staff extended beyond the educational aspects of day-to-day life. I loved having people I could talk with about Sam, people who really seemed to like and care about him. I soon came to value and depend enormously upon the support that I was getting from the staff at Sam's new school.

11

CONFLICT

Having Sam's schooling settled was a relief. My job provided us with enough money to live on. For the first time in years there was no immediate crisis looming on the horizon. Life assumed a calm regularity. I read a great deal, and thought about what I read.

I was intrigued by the idea that conflicting feelings could negate each other and result in a sort of non-action. Conflict in this sense is a central theme of both Niko Tinbergen's and George Victor's books. To me it seemed that their views about the nature of autism had much in common, even though they looked at the condition from different perspectives.

Tinbergen's discussion of approach and avoidance behaviour reveals how the tendency to approach and make social contact can – when contradicted by a simultaneously elicited tendency to withdraw or stay away – result in the 'frozen' postures of autism.

George Victor separates the various strands of behaviour that together form the relationship between a mother and her autistic child. In doing so he shows how a child can become immobilized by contradictory impulses – trapped between his desire to act and his fear of failure.

Both writers agree that autism develops when, in the absence of a secure bond between mother and child, the child's ability to adjust to his environment is overstretched.

Perhaps I was becoming more aware of conflict because it so obviously existed within the context of my own life. I felt that everything I wanted or needed to do was incompatible with something else of equal importance. For example, I longed to improve my work prospects by applying for better jobs, but feared that I would not cope with both Sam and work if my job was more demanding. I also wanted to explore my new-found sociability. For the first time in my life I was enjoying the company of other people, but I could not ignore the fact that Sam hated me going out, and that he saw little enough of me anyway. Sometimes I felt that giving up work and concentrating entirely on him might be the best thing, but that would have meant exchanging our house for a flat and giving up the nice things that my salary bought for us. So I stayed in my well-paid but boring job and spent my weekends quietly at home with Sam. But I resented it. I felt trapped by the circumstances in which we lived, and a failure as a mother.

This conflict was not helped by comments from some work colleagues and friends, who thought that I had been made to 'give up my life' for my handicapped child. Such attitudes hurt me, for although I did sometimes resent Sam, I could not bear for him to be thought of as an 'encumbrance'. I soon learned not to mix with people who looked at him in this light.

Other people commented upon how wonderfully I managed – an autistic child, a full-time job, a big house to look after. I coped the way that I had always done, by strictly controlling my emotions and the patterns of my life. For example, I was obsessional about the way the household was run. Sunday afternoon and evening were almost always spent cleaning, regardless of how tired I felt or how much Sam needed my attention. The house was always tidy, the kitchen immaculate. The paint that was peeling from the window frames and the dangerous state of my car were obliterated from my mind; I controlled a few selected areas absolutely and pushed everything else aside. The future I never considered. The precariousness of our situation, what would happen if either of us became ill, how I would manage when Sam was older – I never allowed these things to surface. Nor did I ever think I might be lonely, or unhappy, or angry with anybody.

On my first visit Dr Read had asked me whether I ever felt that I wanted to hurt anybody. My shocked 'Of course not' was in line with my belief that I was a 'good' person who would not have such wicked thoughts. Then I had believed that it was wrong even to feel rage, but this was no longer true. Now I was often angry – at people in my past, my friends, relatives, all the people who had hurt me – even though I seldom showed these feelings. As my therapy with Dr Read proceeded I found it more and more difficult to keep the lid on my emotions. They simmered away just beneath the surface, threatening to erupt like a volcano. I wanted badly to let go but was afraid of doing so. I became terribly worried about losing control. While I continued to go about my normal business, smiling, agreeing, part of me wanted to scream at people – to tell them what I really thought and to do exactly what I wanted to do. My recurring feeling was of massive blocks of concrete crashing together in my head, shaking me to my bones, smashing the life out of me. The more tightly I controlled my feelings, the more I feared being trapped in the stranglehold of my repressed emotions forever. I should not have been looking after any child at this time, let alone a disturbed, autistic child, but there was nowhere else for Sam to go.

As I careered between despair, unrealistic optimism and the living death of cutting off from my feelings, I thought more about the idea that Sam and I were using the same sort of emotional device. He could be said to have cut himself off much earlier in life than I had, and much more completely. His encapsulation had happened even before he had developed basic skills like relating to people and had crippled his development. I, of course, like other 'normal' people, possessed a range of skills and social abilities, yet I could see that our method of dealing with painful events was similar. We threw a blanket over our emotions, and so avoided feeling the pain. But the price of avoiding hurt in this way is a lack of any real contact with the world. Spontaneity and creativity become impossible, and I could see the rigidity of my own as well as Sam's behaviour. I hated the wooden feeling that I sometimes experienced, and the 'not really there' look that Sam so often wore.

Repression also explained the paradox of Sam's apparent lack of involvement with his environment and his exaggerated but inappropriate emotional responses on other occasions. Dealing with Sam often felt like handling a live mine – just a touch too much pressure in the wrong place at the wrong time and he would explode. His autistic withdrawal continued to be interspersed with periodic emotional outbursts, and the theory that his angry feelings would all be swept into the holding-therapy sessions remained unproven.

My own feelings about holding therapy had become yet another source of conflict for me. I could not seem to make Jennifer understand my concern about the dual messages that I knew Sam was being given. He sensed my anger and insecurity, yet Jennifer and I kept telling him that it was safe for him to lower his defences and that he must do so. By this time I knew how to play the holding-therapy game to perfection – Jennifer even told me that I was her best exponent of the technique. But eventually it became impossible to suppress my realization of the gap between Jennifer's apparent belief in the therapy as a cure-all and my understanding that there was far more to reversing the autistic process than simply knocking down a wall. As a compromise between casting Sam and myself on to the seas of chance without any support at all and continuing with the charade of holding therapy, I asked Jennifer if she would help us in another way. She had told me about a sort of functional learning therapy technique that she had learned from a man called Geoffrey Walden and had used to some effect with her autistic pupil. I understood that it was based upon the idea of the child doing rather than understanding – such things as sorting and matching, and the utilization of both hands when attempting a task were considered important. It sounded useful to me – Sam certainly needed any skills he could be persuaded to acquire. Jennifer agreed to come each Saturday morning to work with Sam, but I felt she was less than happy about my abandoning holding therapy. Understandably so, I suppose, but I no longer believed in it.

Our association with each other staggered on for a time after this but things were never the same again. I thought back over my three years' involvement with Jennifer. It was difficult to gauge the effect of the therapy upon Sam, impossible to tell how he would have been without it. I also wondered whether our experience of this intensely personal therapy might have been different with some other therapist. One of the problems of stepping completely outside any formal discipline and working to the pattern of one individual's ideas, is the absence of any objectivity or any external controlling mechanism. In such a situation, and with the absence of specialist training as a therapist, it would have been almost impossible for Jennifer not to allow her personal feelings to influence the proceedings.

Yet great claims were being made for holding therapy. I read an article in a daily newspaper about a therapist who practised in the south – how her 'controversial treatment was making remarkable progress in the battle against autism'. I felt that this and other publicity the therapist gained implied that holding therapy could cure autism. I was furious. Having done this therapy for so long I understood its limitations, and I also understood the vulnerability of parents of autistic children. Some time later I decided to write an article of my own, which was published in the *Independent* newspaper:

Holding therapists invoke the authority of those involved in the study of body language, like Niko Tinbergen. They also include amongst their mentors well-known child psychiatrists such as D. W. Winnicott and John Bowlby, whose *Attachment and Loss* is considered by many to be the definitive work on early childhood development. Although these influential figures agree that the mother-child bond is all-important and that an unsatisfactory bond can adversely affect a child's development, this does not necessarily mean that their scholarly works are proof of the efficacy of holding therapy. Of course there is evidence that autists are adopting an extreme defensive manoeuvre – researchers who have studied the body language of these children have found that their behaviour can be perceived as existing almost entirely of avoidance techniques. It is only when viewed in this context that the extraordinary behaviour of autism can be seen to make any sense at all. Once it is recognized as the ultimate defence, the castle wall that surrounds the terrified self, seemingly inexplicable postures and attitudes can be seen to constitute a logical, if aberrant, system of behaviour. But to assume that because a condition is basically an emotional one it can be cured by forcing the expression of emotion, requires nothing less than an act of faith. This is precisely what is asked of parents when they embark upon holding therapy. To make such a leap of the imagination is to reduce human development, intricate and complex as it is, to an absurdly simplistic level.

I did holding therapy with my autistic child for three years. In the early stages he released a great deal of repressed anger and seemed more relaxed at the end of a session. The therapy helped us both to get in touch with our emotions. This initial 'honeymoon' period was almost inevitable however, considering our emotional state at the time. We had all been living in a turmoil of anxious uncertainty for several years when we were offered both support and hope by the holding therapist. The relief, and the need to believe in the treatment, were overwhelming. The therapist was adamant – our son would recover. But sometime during our first year of therapy I realized that my son was no longer experiencing the joy of being allowed to express his natural feelings. Now he was being forced to become angry because somebody had decided that he should, which is very different. I began to feel my child was increasing his resistance to my approaches – the more he resisted, the more I was told to push him. This led to us becoming locked into a situation of almost unbearable tension; spontaneity disappeared from our holding sessions as I increased my efforts to do what was required of me. I felt a failure, which in turn made me feel I must try harder. It was a very vicious circle.

We continued with the therapy far beyond the point at which it ceased to be helpful. Our therapist convinced me that it would be harmful to my son if I stopped – she said he would feel I no longer cared enough to hold him. In turn I felt she was the only person who understood my son and believed he would get better. As far as I knew she offered the only help available that at least attempted a cure. After I stopped doing the therapy it took me a long time before I was able to see the whole experience in perspective. Looking back I was appalled by some of the things we had done. The therapist should not have assumed responsibility for two very vulnerable lives when she had neither the training nor the experience to support her good intentions. Neither should she have assured us that our child would recover, with no evidence to back this up. Eventually I realized I was trying to force my son to confront feelings with which he was not equipped to deal. Having adopted the psychologically crippling defence of autism, my son's response to our attempts to blast a way through his protective wall was to withdraw even further. Holding therapy, I concluded, can be dangerous.

Jennifer and I had parted company at least a year before I wrote this article. At the time it felt rather like a divorce. Although we had met only once a week we had talked often and at great length on the telephone – discussing autism, emotional disturbance, psychological development, and Sam. I felt very involved with her. Jennifer represented my one hope for my son; she was a central part of our lives.

We stopped doing holding therapy when Sam was seven years old. As Jennifer drove away for the last time – her car filled with the various pieces of equipment that she had loaned us over the years – I felt very sad. Although we had met only three years before, the emotional experiences that we had shared during the holding-therapy sessions meant that we had got to know each other well. I was anxious as well, and worried about how I would manage without her. But I also felt a sense of freedom, for now I was no longer constrained by having to try to fit my own developing ideas about autism into the holding-therapy framework.

Ironically, the final separation between Jennifer and me had come about because of a book she had lent me. In fact she did not seem terribly enthusiastic about it, but suggested I might be interested anyway. The book was called *Autism and Childhood Psychosis*, the author, Frances Tustin. After reading it I got in touch with Frances Tustin – to my amazement it was as easy as picking up the telephone. We talked for a long time, and she agreed to see Sam, to determine whether she thought he would respond to psychotherapeutic treatment.

Whether I was just moving on to a new mentor, or whether it was sound judgement that made me recognize Frances Tustin's profound understanding of the autistic condition, I do not know. But I did realize that an involvement with psychotherapy would mean a final end to our holding therapy, and so our association with Jennifer. Perhaps there are times when different types of treatment can complement each other, but these two would not have meshed. Although both attempt to deal with basic emotional issues, the fundamental approach is quite different.

Holding therapists pre-suppose that the child is angry, and encourage/force him to express that anger. Psychotherapists, on the other hand, do not believe that the child should be forced to show his feelings, but if and when he does decide to do so, then the therapist makes a point of acknowledging his words and actions.

Perhaps holding therapy had appealed to me because I wanted so much to let go of my own emotions. But I had come to see that a lifetime of repressed thoughts and feelings cannot be flushed out in a great emotional outburst. Patterns of behaviour need to be painstakingly altered – this had been my own experience, and I felt that it must be so for Sam as well.

Whether holding therapy harmed or helped Sam I shall never know. Certainly he made some progress during the three years that we did it, but then he would almost certainly have done so anyway. Holding therapy did help me to become aware of my feelings, but that in itself was no cure for my son's autism. To me it still seems far too simplistic a device for dealing with the complexities of autistic withdrawal. Yet despite my ambivalence towards the therapy and my mixed feelings regarding our involvement with Jennifer I knew that it was she who had helped me to believe that Sam was sensitive, intelligent, and ultimately savable. For that I was grateful.

12

PSYCHOTHERAPY

I was very excited about our visit to Frances Tustin. She had worked with autistic children for thirty years, during which time she had come to understand a great deal about how they functioned. She found that the insights she gained suggested ways in which psychotherapists could get in touch with these apparently unreachable children — even those who, like Sam, did not have any language.

I already felt sure that Sam needed psychological help of one kind or another. Even Lucy who had no more than a pragmatic interest in emotional matters felt that he should have some sort of therapy to help him. I felt his withdrawal and behavioural problems were definitely linked to our relationship; that was clear from the way his autistic symptoms waxed and waned in relation to the situation at home. The degree to which my state of mind seemed to affect Sam often amazed me. If I became tense through feeling hurt or angry about something, Sam would become obsessive, and his futile attempts to control his environment by controlling an arbitrary aspect of it were very familiar to me. If we went for a walk feeling happy and relaxed with each other we would laugh and run and enjoy ourselves. If either one of us was anxious, Sam would immediately lock himself into a grass-picking obsession, pulling handfuls then letting it drop slowly through his fingers as he stared at it, wearing a fixed, wooden expression as he did so. Although I had tried very hard to strengthen the tenuous bond between us, and our relationship had improved, he and I were still either enmeshed with each other or worlds apart. We held on to each other too tightly, then rejected each other too violently when we got hurt. The problem was exacerbated by our total dependence on each other. Sam needed somebody of his own, someone who was nothing to do with me to whom perhaps he could learn to relate in a different way.

In my years of dealing with members of the medical profession, the local health authority and the Autistic Society, I had never heard mention of psychotherapy as a treatment for autism. I was therefore surprised to learn that Frances Tustin had published several books which in France and Italy were considered to be standard works on the subject. It seemed that she was valued less in her own country than she was abroad, where she had worked and lectured extensively. I had come across her purely by chance, and at first, I thought, too late. She was now in her seventies and no longer practising as a therapist, although she did still write. She also felt that Sam was a little old to begin treatment, preferring children to be below six years of age when they started with her. However, she had at least agreed to see us.

I wanted this help for Sam, and set about trying to determine the sort of child Mrs Tustin considered suitable for treatment. There was about a month between the time of our conversation and our appointment. I knew that when the time came I would be quite prepared to say anything, tell any lies, that might improve Sam's chances of getting psychotherapy. I went carefully through *Autism and Childhood Psychosis* looking for clues as to what I should say about him.

In this book Frances Tustin examines the primitive states of mind that exist in the human infant before the socializing influence of relationships with other people link him to the world of commonly agreed reality. I found *Autism and Childhood Psychosis* hard going at first. It was rather like entering another world. Frances Tustin points out the difficulties inherent in trying to describe the experiences that occur in this strange, pre-verbal, dream-like stage, where shapes and forms loom large in importance and bear little relation to the thoughts and feelings familiar to us. She describes states of mind that have for most of us been overlaid and forgotten during the process of normal psychological development; from a consciousness that consists entirely of basic needs and their fulfilment or the lack of it, we have gradually acquired the hierarchy of concepts and the sophisticated array of emotional responses that we take for granted. Frances Tustin explains how and why the autistic child remains 'stuck' in the first stage of primitive awareness, and examines the steps that he fails for a variety of reasons to take.

I had by this time come across the ideas of the well-known child psychiatrist D. W. Winnicott. From him I learned how the developing child is drawn into the world by having his desire for food fulfilled, his quest for affirmation satisfied by his mother's smiling face, and his need for boundaries to his world supplied by the arms that hold him and the caring attention that protects him. In this way the totally dependent infant who has no sense of his own self develops first a sense of himself as separate from his mother, then a sense of his own identity and capabilities. Had I not been familiar with these ideas of how a child normally develops, the distortions which Frances Tustin writes about would have been perplexing indeed.

Her language is evocative rather than theoretical, her descriptions metaphorical rather than literal. She believes, together with many other psychologists and psychiatrists, that we are born with the potential for psychological development in the same way that a foetus has the potential to develop into a human being. Frances Tustin describes this potential in terms of 'innate forms' – sort of flexible moulds into which experience is cast. When an innate form corresponds with a received experience, the child has the illusion that everything is continuous with his own body stuff. When it does not, either he grows psychologically to accommodate the new experience, or, if this would require emotional responses and structures which have not yet developed, he withdraws from it. To put this another way: in the early stages of development a child encounters basically two types of experience – that which is familiar and that which is not. As he matures he learns to cope with that which is not and so increases his repertoire of abilities, but at the beginning of life his ability to adapt is very limited. If unbearably unfamiliar experience is thrust upon him too early he is traumatized. He shuts it out in a total and rigid way – he adopts an autistic defence.

Another aspect of Frances Tustin's work that interested me was the way she attempted to categorize autistic children into different types. It is sometimes difficult to discern a link between children who seem very different from each other yet have all been described as autistic. Now I could see that the link is the type of process these children adopt to deal with their experiences; the differences between them are due to the degree to which the defence has been adopted and the stage of development at which it occurred.

Children who seem totally cut off from the world are described by Frances Tustin as being of the 'encapsulated' type. These are the children who have the classic symptoms of non-communicativeness and withdrawal and are most easily recognized as autistic. They have isolated themselves completely from the world at a very early age, and so have remained in a primitive state of awareness. They have developed neither abilities, nor concepts, nor even a sense of their own identities. Other children may have had a phase of normal development before adopting an autistic defence, or they may have isolated only certain parts of their personalities. These children appear more normal than the seemingly unreachable, encapsulated children, for they may have some language and some points of contact with reality.

Yet although they function at a higher level, their personalities are more confused. The development of this type of child has been badly distorted, while in the classically autistic encapsulated child it has hardly even begun. The encapsulated child often functions at a very low level, and as well as seeming unreachable he is often assumed to be unteachable. I learned that these were the children that Frances Tustin preferred to treat, and that she had helped some of them to the point where they were able to live normal lives.

From the clear definitions Mrs Tustin made between different types of autistic children it was obvious that she was able to determine much from a description of the child's symptoms. She did not want to examine Sam as I had expected she would when we went to visit her. In fact she seemed more interested in hearing about him – about his past and present behaviour – and about myself. It was marvellous to talk to somebody who listened and believed what I said about Sam's and my relationship. Frances Tustin did not try to protect me by implying that the reason for our present situation was somehow Sam's fault, but neither did she criticize when I related some of the experiences that had obviously been harmful to him. My story seemed to make sense to her. She was neither surprised nor shocked – simply accepting. I did not feel the need to lie – of course it would have been utterly pointless anyway – for Sam seemed to be a classic case of the encapsulated autistic child.

Mrs Tustin explained that one of her reasons for making this assessment was the fact that he carried what she called an 'autistic object'. An autistic object is a hard object clutched obsessively in the child's hand. Unlike a toy or teddy to which a child may be attached, it does not serve any purpose other than to provide the sensation experienced by the child as he presses it into his hand. Its function is to create the illusion of continuity that these children crave. The child presses then feels the pressure, presses then feels, presses then feels. This creates the closed circuit that should have occurred naturally between mother and child during his first few weeks of life, but which did not do so.

Sam had carried a small hard object since he was two years old. I remembered how he had first clutched his helicopter at all times, and this had been followed by a succession of cars and planes, sticks, kitchen utensils and household items. Other than the helicopter and one or two particular cars, the objects did not seem to be important in themselves. If one was mislaid, for example, Sam might panic for a few minutes, but then it would be replaced by another, which soon became equally important – not as a toy to be played with, but as an object to be held. I had always vaguely assumed that Sam carried things 'for security', but was interested to learn of the real significance behind his apparently meaningless habit.

There were other behaviours that Frances Tustin recognized as symptoms of the 'total withdrawal from a very early age' type of autism, and Sam seemed to have them all. She cited a good aptitude for pattern recognition as being important. Sam certainly had this. During the first few months of his life he would become wildly excited by patterns and textures. I have a photograph of him at about six weeks gazing wide-eyed and stretching towards a cushion cover on which was embroidered a flower design. I remember the occasion well. He quivered all over as he looked at the cushion, and continued to do so for many months afterwards whenever it caught his eye. As a baby he also loved the graphic design on the breakfast cereal packet. For months he would not settle at bedtime unless it was propped up so that he could see it from his carrycot. Even later when his behaviour was distorted by the layers of autism, Sam's interest in patterns was apparent. Lucy had persevered in getting him to sit still long enough to do a jigsaw puzzle, and this was the one area of activity in which he performed normally for his age.

The idea that these children are hypersensitive to sensory stimulation also fitted with my experience with Sam, as well as the observation that they often make a palpable barrier of some kind, both to exclude sensation itself and also to block out an awareness of the world. During those first few years when I had pushed Sam for mile after mile in his buggy, he would often cover his ears. Sometimes he would cover his eyes, or even put his arms over his head. I never understood this, and frequently felt embarrassed by it. He was also terrified of certain noises. The hum of his spinning top would cause him to flee in panic, or the sound of a toy trumpet to scream in fear.

Frances Tustin believed a good memory to be a diagnostic sign of encapsulated autism, and I knew that Sam possessed this. Nobody else believed it, there was after all none of the usual evidence like the ability to recite tables or remember spelling, but living with Sam I knew that he remembered some things extraordinarily well. If we visited a place to which we had not been for many years, for example, Sam would go straight to a particular toy or object that had interested him previously. Or he would take me to fetch an object from a place where it might have been sitting, forgotten by me for many months, until he suddenly wanted it for some reason.

And then there was the constant seeking of analogies. Sam's delight in finding that a thing resembled something else had always been apparent, and was in itself a source of delight for me. I remembered his bib-beard comparison. It had seemed such a strange comparison to make, but he linked the two things because their shapes were similar – both were crescent-shaped objects that hung beneath the chin. Another one that puzzled me for many months was a shot in the opening sequence of a television soap opera which Sam found wildly exciting. It was just a collection of rooftops and chimneys but at the first bar of the theme music he would rush off to get his little wooden Christmas tree. It was clear that he saw some similarity – he would hold his tree out to the television when this scene appeared and smile – but I could not see what it was. Eventually I did. The roofs were seen in long perspective and if the content and meaning of the image was disregarded then their outline did resemble the shape of a Christmas tree. Shapes were important to Sam.

By the time we went to see Frances Tustin I was desperate to get help for my son. He had been alive for seven years, yet he seemed to be stranded in a body that continued to grow with a mind that was locked off in time. His speech was almost non-existent, being no more than a few almost unrecognizable words which were used only occasionally. He could not really dress himself. He played a little – he would run the toy cars along his road mat or join up the track of his wooden train set – but never for very long. If left to his own devices he would often indulge in some sort of obsessive cutting-off activity, like picking bits of fluff from the carpet or grinding his teeth. He took no more than a passing interest in television, although occasionally a car chase or air battle would attract his attention and sometimes he might watch a nature programme for a short time. He would hold a pencil but was a long way from learning to write, even though he could by this time draw a cross and a ladder. It worried me terribly that Sam had no means by which to express himself, neither verbal nor written, nor even through play. His acquisition of skills seemed hardly to have increased at all, yet he was becoming more difficult to live with. Since moving to his new school he had begun to open up a little in his attitude towards other people and the manipulation he was trying with his teacher was also in evidence at home.

When Sam was in manipulative mood he could be relentless and infuriating. He would stand at the top of the stairs, hurling things down and shouting 'bad boy' with his own unique and barely distinguishable pronunciation. Or he would hold aloft some object like a glass or pot plant, looking wildly at me and threatening to throw it, again to the accompaniment of his 'bad boy' war cry. Sometimes when we were out he would roll his head about with his mouth open, looking completely idiotic. He would watch me out of the corner of his eye while he did this, no doubt noting with glee my acute discomfort and repressed fury. His development may have been retarded but he certainly knew how to manipulate people, often without them even realizing it.

Although this sort of thing was very difficult to deal with, it did not upset me as much as Sam's cutting-off behaviour. To see him staring fixedly at an object held two inches from the end of his nose drove me absolutely frantic. He still did this sometimes and when he did I could see that his overt attempts to control me were indeed signs of progress. The manipulation was like an alien presence taking charge of my body and scrambling my brain, but the cutting off felt like a cloak of death being cast over the two of us.

I wanted help for Sam for his own sake, but also I wanted to share the responsibility for him with somebody else. It had been arranged that I should ring Frances Tustin several days after our meeting. When I did she told me that Sam was the type of autistic child that she considered to be most treatable. This was good news. The bad news was that the only psychotherapeutic help available to him would be in London, which was over two hundred miles from where we lived. It would have to be private, and thus expensive. Also, the treatment would inevitably be less effective than with a child who was starting younger and having it more frequently. Mrs Tustin had never treated such a child on a once-a-week basis before. It would normally be between two and five times a week, but our circumstances would make this impossible. However, if I could accommodate all these matters, she did know a therapist who would see Sam on a weekly basis under her supervision.

The visit to Frances Tustin had a profound effect upon me. During the past seven years I had tried increasingly to see Sam's autism objectively, but at the same time another part of me had refused to look at or think about *him*. For years I had not had any real idea of what was wrong with my son, but even when I had begun to gain a scanty knowledge of the nature of his problems it had still been possible to believe that he would get better. Piecing together the jigsaw of understanding what was wrong with Sam, I had come to feel that when the puzzle was complete he would somehow recover. Now I could no longer avoid seeing that this was not the case, nor escape thinking about the future. At the time I wrote in my diary:

We have been to visit Frances Tustin. Both reading her book and the thoughts and feelings subsequently stimulated by our visit have changed my life. I can no longer avoid Sam – what has happened to him, the way he is now, the immense problems he had, his suffering, and the unlikelihood of his getting better. I have cut off my feelings about him really since he was born.

It was painful also to acknowledge that I had for years spent so much time and energy trying to get help for Sam and only now, when he was nearly seven and a half years old, when it was quite possibly too late, had I managed to find the sort of help he needed. I had always dreaded the hopeless frustration of the 'help came too late' syndrome, which was why I had pressed for a diagnosis for Sam when he was two and a half years old. Much good it had done me, or him.

But now there was an opportunity of help for him, and I was determined that he was going to be able to use it. I thought through the various possibilities. The most obvious solution would have been to move to London, but the idea of destroying the life I had so painstakingly constructed filled me with such horror that I eventually abandoned it. Our home and my job were all the security that Sam and I had. The other alternative was to go down to London each week. I approached my employer and asked whether I might work flexitime – four long days to accommodate my taking Monday off. He generously agreed. Lucy also said she would fit in with our new arrangements.

The cost of the train journey and the therapy I could just about manage, but we lived a good half-hour's drive from the station and our car would have to spend the day in the station car park. This I could not afford. I made an appointment with the stationmaster. During my interview he was called out to an emergency in the railyard, so our discussion took place as we walked along the track. I explained my case, and obviously struck a chord. He nodded sagely – a kind and sympathetic man – then agreed to ease my burden by allowing us free parking in the short-stay car park right by the station entrance. And so it was all arranged. We caught a morning train from Leeds to King's Cross and then took the tube across London to the therapist's consulting rooms near Finchley Road.

Lisa was a qualified psychotherapist with experience of autistic children. She had been found for us by Frances Tustin, with whom she was having weekly supervision. She saw Sam for fifty minutes on Monday afternoon, then telephoned Frances Tustin on Tuesday so that they could discuss Sam's therapy session in detail. I would then telephone Frances on Wednesday, and she would tell me some of what had happened during the session and how she and Lisa had interpreted it. As I learned through Mrs Tustin about how things were going, I had very little contact with Lisa herself. Our exchanges were limited to greetings at the beginning and end of each session. The therapy was for Sam alone – I was not to be involved.

While Sam was off with her I would sit in the waiting room wondering what was going on, listening for clues. It was a nice room with plenty of books and plants and an enormous plane tree outside the window. I watched the seasons come and go in that tree, waiting for I know not what. There was never anybody in the room but me. Sometimes I read, working my way through the bookshelves, but usually I daydreamed. Dreams of being rich and paying somebody to make Sam better, or of writing a book about him, a book with a happy ending, a story of complete recovery.

I enjoyed this time on my own. Apart from anything else it provided a short respite between the trauma of the journey down and the return journey yet to be faced. I found the embarrassment Sam caused me the most difficult thing to bear. At this time he was still carrying his helicopter, and had recently become preoccupied by the idea of it going up into the sky. He would hold it above his head, stretching on tiptoe as he shouted 'Up, up, up!' excitedly – a lone voice amongst the businessmen and rustling newspapers. Of course other children played, but not like Sam. His behaviour was so odd, and did not match his age and size. I should not have cared, but I did. I longed not to worry what people thought almost more than I wished Sam would not give rise to my distress in the first place.

Sometimes we would stand looking out of the window at the end of the carriage watching the countryside rush by. Sam loved to feel the air beating against his face and so would struggle with me to keep the window open, whatever the weather. We had some hair-raising moments. I soon gave up taking jigsaws because he would fling the puzzle all over the carriage if he could not find the piece that he wanted. Once he tipped a carton of orange juice over the man in front. Often he surprised our fellow passengers with his repertoire of strange noises. The journey down was not too bad but coming back could be wearing. Sam was fed up, and I was tired. On the whole, though, he was really very good. It was a lot of travelling to do in one day for a little boy who must have wondered why, and what on earth it was all for.

13

COMING ALIVE

Life started to open out a little for Sam and myself during Sam's eighth year. Until then he had always been unwilling to let me out of his sight, and when we did have to part, his way of dealing with the situation was quite unlike the obvious display of unhappiness that a normal child would show. Sam would not cling or cry. Instead he would set his face in an expressionless mask, behaving as though I did not exist. Then I began to notice that he was sometimes coping with me being absent for short periods without doing this. For example, if I left the room to fetch something, he would continue with what he was doing for the few minutes that I was away rather than sinking into obsessive behaviour as soon as I left him.

I could see how important it was that Sam should have events in his life that belonged to him alone if he was ever to develop a sense of his own identity. We lived near a riding school, and I had for some time been meaning to arrange for Sam to have lessons. I had put off approaching Pat, the owner of the school, fearing that she might find Sam too daunting a prospect. She did not. Pat was an outspoken, no-nonsense person who inspired confidence with her enthusiasm. I was amazed when she got Sam on a horse after only one session, for this was the child who ran terrified from our domestic cat.

Pat would lead Sam on Tally, an elderly brown horse who was called out of retirement to transport Sam around the field each Sunday morning. During the lessons I sat on the grass under a tree while Pat ran up and down beside Tally and Sam, shouting instructions as she went. 'Hold the reins, Sam. Sit up straight. Kick, kick.'

I loved watching Sam being taught to do something. He could see me all the time and when he got to the farthest end of the field he would turn and crane his neck to check that I was still there. Sam hated having anything on his head, and at first his refusal to wear a riding hat threatened to be a problem. I thought that the whole arrangement might be toppled by this sticking point, but Pat was very persuasive. Sam eventually complied and wore his hat.

During those first few months Pat tested Sam's capabilities in various ways. His balance was good, she said, which was useful. Riding with his hands above his head, lying back in the saddle – these things seemed to come easily to him. Getting Sam to listen to what was being said was a different matter. Pat soon found that gaining Sam's attention was one of the major problems. He obviously found the experience of riding enjoyable, but this incentive was not enough to make him tune in and learn about what he was doing in the way most children would.

I could also see another difficulty, one which a person unfamiliar with autism might not recognize. Sam had no belief whatsoever in his ability to control an animal. He simply could not conceive of such a thing, having no confidence in his capacity to do anything at all. Although he sometimes did do what Pat asked him, I felt sure he imagined it was she who somehow controlled the horse. This was probably why Sam took so long to learn that he must hold the reins – he just did not see the point of doing so.

After several months of these one-to-one lessons, Pat felt it was worth trying Sam with the group. The riding lessons alternated between a teaching session in the field one week and a trek over hills and moorland the next. The first time that Sam set off on his trek with just a young girl leading his horse I was terrified. But Pat assured me that he would be all right, and he was. I worried too much, she said.

Sam moved surprisingly quickly from being afraid to go near any horse to being willing to ride whichever of the horses was available. Of course he was always on a leading rein, but this did not stop some of the other children from refusing to go on the bigger animals. I am sure that Sam felt safe because he believed that Pat was firmly in control of everything, including the behaviour of her animals. Two and a half years later Sam learned to mount his horse alone and to rise to the trot. He still needs a leader, but he has at last begun to use a firmer grip in holding the reins. Perhaps he has seen the glimmer of a possibility that he might one day be able to take charge of the operation.

I was pleased to have established Sam's Sunday morning riding lessons, for now that we no longer spent our Saturdays doing holding therapy, we had more time to fill at the weekends. I tried to make some sort of pattern because I had come to accept that any child – but especially a child like Sam – needs a routine.

Saturday morning we usually shopped for food, and Sam could make this a hellish event. Hand poised, he would threaten to sweep things from the shelves, or squirm about in an awkward way just missing the displays of goods and the other shoppers. His wandering off down aisles of the supermarket infuriated me, especially considering his unwillingness to leave my side at other times. Here he knew that I would follow him, and I always did, anticipating his panic if he lost sight of me. This had happened in a department store once. I lost track of Sam for a minute, only to have his whereabouts pinpointed by the screams that emanated from the spot where he had sunk writhing to the floor, accompanied by a rack of ladies' nighties.

We usually went to the swimming pool at some point, which Sam loved, and often for a long walk as well. We both liked walking and would tramp up the steep incline opposite our house, then wander through the woods at the top. Sam liked exploring, and would try to drag me down winding lanes and impassable tracks. This reminded me of my own childhood, when I used to venture off alone for whole days at a time. I always wanted to go up the next hill, across the next creek, over the next rocky outcrop. I used to feel as though I was looking for something, but I never found it. Whether Sam had the same feeling I do not know, but he always wanted to discover the half-hidden pathways that were off our beaten track, often to the point of perversity.

Although Sam and I usually spent our weekends alone, I was beginning to make tentative connections with the outside world. One of the people I became friendly with was Laura, another mother of an autistic child. Distance prevented us from meeting very often, but we used to compare notes on the telephone.

I was interested to hear about Laura's experiences with her

son Christopher. Christopher had seemed to develop normally for several years before regressing to an autistic state six months after the birth of a sister when he was about four. Christopher lost all his speech and started behaving like a severely retarded child. For a long time Laura was in despair. Then she began to feel that her son was understanding more than he showed. She decided to try teaching him to read, using the Glen Doman method. This involves the mother holding up a large card on which is printed a word, which she says, smiling at her child as she does so. This procedure is repeated at frequent intervals throughout the day, and is apparently quite successful in building a reading vocabulary. Christopher did learn to read, and from that time he made good progress.

I was impressed by Laura's story, which also gave me hope that my son too might improve. Laura had put a great deal of effort into helping Christopher, and much of what she did seemed to have been just what he needed.

Laura told me about the little books that she and Christopher used to make, cataloguing the events of a particular day, in which they stuck bus tickets, wrote names of places visited and so on. This sounded ideal for fostering a sense of time and place, and thus a sense of identity. And the Glen Doman method, aimed at teaching children to read, clearly had other advantages too. The regular eye contact that was specifically linked to a pleasant experience that recurred many times during the day must surely have played an important part in drawing Christopher back into the world of human activities, and re-establishing a bond between him and his mother.

Although Laura did not cure her son's autism, she did pull him several rungs up the ladder in a fairly short space of time. I tried to do with Sam some of the activities that Laura described, but I could not manage them. For one thing Sam and I were apart all day, but in any case, I myself was just not confident enough to do such things. I could not bear Sam's continual rejection when I tried to teach him anything, and I did not have the emotional support of a partner.

Unlike Sam, Christopher is now in many respects like other children of his own age. He reads and writes, has interests and hobbies. He attends a normal school with only a part-time special assistant to help him. Yet his personality is still profoundly affected and distorted by his autism. He communicates with other people, but he seems somehow out of step. His intelligence is not broad-ranging like that of a normal child, but is tightly controlled and used only in certain areas like his school work or his special interests. For example, he is not able to converse in a free-flowing and normal manner, and his social skills are limited. Like Sam, Christopher seems unbothered by his social gaffs. He appears not to care what other people think of him. He also has obsessional habits that drive his mother to distraction, in the same way that Sam's grass-picking does me.

A child like Sam who has cut off at a very early stage of development is perhaps harder to make sense of than a more able child like Christopher. Sam is so withdrawn and does so little that it is difficult to isolate his areas of weakness. With Christopher, on the other hand, the autistic behaviour is spotlighted. It stands out in dramatic relief against his normal academic achievement. The nature of his problem is defined still further by the type of help he needs in class. His school work he can do fairly easily; what he requires is someone to act as a sort of social buffer. When the teacher speaks from the front of the class Christopher needs somebody to 'catch the words' and give them to him. He is not deaf, and he is not unable to comprehend. But the distance between himself and the teacher, and the fact that her words are not aimed directly at him, seem to make it impossible for Christopher to gather the sense of what she is saying. He cannot bridge the gap between the two of them.

It is not that autistic children cannot understand. It is just that experiences which do not dovetail neatly and easily with their own mental and emotional situation are immediately rejected. If something does not fit they cut off rather than stretch to accommodate what is new.

The information had to be fed into Christopher by someone who was close to him physically and mentally, who could tailor it to fit his mind. Even though Sam functions at a much lower level than Christopher I can see the same mechanisms at work in him. His terms of reference are more restricted and so the fit needs to be even more precise in order to get through to him. For years he appeared not to hear what was being said to him unless one held his face and talked gently but directly to him, and even then he paid attention only to a very limited range of subjects.

The day when Laura and her family came to visit us for the first time was not easy for either me or Sam, for we had grown quite unused to visitors. I felt extremely nervous and Sam ground his teeth and tensed his body, waiting for the moment when they would go away. This was the very reason why I had discouraged people from coming to see us for so long. Yet I was beginning to realize how much we needed other people in our lives. I felt sure that another family with an autistic child could somehow be easier to form a friendship with, and they did understand some of our problems in a way that nobody else could. Sam and I both felt a sense of achievement after one of these visits – at least, I know I did, and he seemed to as well. He would close the door purposefully when they left, but with a pleased look on his face. We were doing something normal, behaving like ordinary people. As soon as they had gone Sam would repossess all the toys that had been played with by Christopher and Ellen. He would touch everything they had used, and play frantically with whatever it was that they had most favoured. I would set about straightening the house, and cleaning up in the kitchen, making things just as they were before our visitors had come. How alike Sam and I were.

By the time our new friends had been to see us a few times, Sam had begun to relax a little. He was always happier if we went out for a walk or to the playground, as using energy seemed to help diffuse his anxiety. But Sam and Christopher never did play together, even though they were the same age. How could they? They both needed far more than normal from the person they were interacting with, and each of them had less than normal to give.

Sam's only taste of friendship was with Tim, the little boy at school who had taken a liking to him. Not only had I seen them together in rough-and-tumble play, but Mrs Thompson often told me about how Tim looked after Sam. I was very happy about this relationship, and arranged for Tim to come and stay for a weekend. Tim's problems were quite different from Sam's. Although his development was retarded he did speak and communicate in the normal way. It was odd having someone around who kept up a stream of chatter which prevented me from slipping off into my own world, and it made me aware how little I spoke to Sam.

That Sam and Tim were going to need a great deal of help if we were to survive the weekend soon became apparent. They could only cope with each other in short bursts; Sam was wildly excited and wanted to roll around on the floor laughing and pulling Tim into his game, but Tim soon needed to retreat. He quickly got bored with the game – it was the only one that Sam knew – and wanted to go off and investigate Sam's toys. That Tim must have felt insecure being in a strange place was brought home to me by an incident later in the day. Tim's vest was wet and I had given him one of Sam's to change into. He disappeared upstairs with it but I noticed when he came down that he had not changed. On checking his room I found that Tim had secreted the clean vest along with the remains of our lunchtime sandwiches and my discarded chocolate wrapper in the bottom of his bag. He had also carefully stored away his share of the balloons I had divided between him and Sam, and the sweets I had given to him. Nothing was used or consumed, everything was saved for later. He seemed so poverty-stricken and defenceless, and yet Tim was at least trying to construct his world by amassing some things for himself. Sam could not even have done this. Although he had started feeling possessive about his toys he would never have reclaimed one of them from another child. Neither would he have attempted to protect his interests in the way that Tim was doing. Sam's method of dealing with a situation such as the one Tim was in would be to withdraw completely by concentrating his attention obsessively upon one tiny object.

Looked at superficially, the relationship between Tim and Sam did not develop beyond a fairly primitive level. For example, Sam's only way of expressing his attitude towards his friend was to rampage in a wildly excited state around the room when I said that he was coming to stay. There is no doubt that he had strong feelings and a sense of involvement with Tim, but what exactly he felt I could not know. The relationship must from Sam's point of view have contained a large element of fantasy, because he and Tim actually interacted very little with each other. They did not really play together, apart from the rough-and-tumble play, but I noticed the way that Sam watched Tim closely without appearing to look at him. Autistic children are said to use peripheral vision far more than other people – it is a way of observing without appearing to be doing so – and I could see the process in action.

During the weekend when he stayed and on other occasions when Tim came to visit, I took dozens of photographs of him and Sam together. Sam has never tired of looking at them. His relationship with Tim was tremendously important to Sam and I did everything that I could to foster it.

For much of our time at home together Sam and I were still each locked into our own private worlds. Once I started making friends at work and going out more, the contrast between life in the outside world and that at home was more marked. I wanted to bring the different strands of my life together. I wanted Sam to be involved with my friends, but being with him and other people still made me anxious. I found the conflicting demands of attending to Sam and conversing with my friends almost impossible to negotiate. I had always felt that way. From the time our son was born I sensed that Peter resented the way that Sam took so much of my attention. I would feel guilty when relating to Sam, but just as bad about turning my attention elsewhere, and so 'neglecting' him. The way that some mothers seem able to attend to their children and converse with a third party at the same time fascinates me. I have often watched such women in an effort to see how it is done, but still find it difficult.

The few people who did become a part of our lives were those who persisted despite my rejecting behaviour. One friend, Jake, made a great effort to form a relationship with Sam. But Sam did not want anyone else in our lives. If a friend came to visit me during the evening when he was officially in bed, he would throw toys around in his bedroom, crashing and banging until eleven or twelve at night. During this period (it lasted for many months) he ripped everything from his walls and broke many toys. On his bedroom door was a large plastic-sealed photograph of him and me sitting together, and one of the most disturbing things that he used to do was to screw up this print and shove it under his bed. Few things have made me feel so annihilated.

It seemed then as though Sam would do anything to prevent me from forming relationships with other people. He appeared not to want to relate to me himself, but he did not want anybody else to do so either. I used to get very angry with his destructive, tyrannical behaviour, and sometimes lost my temper and smacked him. Immediately I would feel guilty. He would not have behaved in such an extreme manner had he not felt insecure, and I should not have hit him. But it always happened so quickly – a flash of fury like a sword swipe before I had the chance to stop it. Then I would feel terrible, and determined never to smack him again.

Sometimes when Sam and I went walking with Jake and his dog, Pluto, things worked out quite well. As when Laura and her family had visited, I felt a great sense of achievement the first time that we did this. We had literally never before been out together with anybody other than Peter or relatives. I remember the occasion well. Sam and I had both been nervous before Jake's arrival that day. As we all walked along the riverbank I found myself juggling as usual, trying to share my attention between Sam and Jake. Although he showed nothing I think that Sam would have loved Jake to approach and talk to him, but Jake was daunted by Sam's apparent unresponsiveness. It made me think about the many times that Sam, Peter and myself had done this same walk. Peter would always walk on ahead while Sam fell further and further behind. I would be torn between the two, forever trying to bridge the gap.

Peter still came each fourth weekend to see Sam, and as he no longer lived in the area he sometimes stayed at the house. This created a strangely unreal domestic situation for the two days that he was there. Sam seemed to like having his father at home, but it must have been very confusing for him. I could not decide whether he was better off with this contact with his father or not, for Sam could not tell me how he felt. To make the weekend work at all I had to be constantly aware of both Peter and Sam, and to balance the attention that I gave to each of them. Then sometimes I would see how happy they could be together, and how much they had to give each other. For months at a time Peter would be determined to repair the damaged relationship between himself and Sam. I would feel hopeful about Sam having a father figure that he could rely upon, which I knew he needed. Then things would go wrong. Peter would become angry and resentful, making Sam tense, withdrawn and obsessive. Sometimes Peter decided he did not want to see Sam for long periods, and then I felt guilty for having allowed my son to be hurt yet again. We seemed to go around in circles, with Peter wanting to be involved with Sam, visiting regularly and trying to stay 'in touch' with him, then pulling away again and destroying what he had built. I could not seem to take a firm stand either. I was probably afraid of assuming total responsibility for my son, but I also knew that we would all benefit from any improvement in the relationship between Peter and Sam.

At this time I was reading the work of Dr Alice Miller. She writes in *For Your Own Good* about the way one generation infects the next by passing down the burden of anger and repression through destructive child-rearing practices. Parents beat their children, either physically or mentally, in an attempt to regain the power over their lives that they lost to their own parents. For example a child is told that he must do something 'for his own good'. When his instinctive reaction against the instruction clashes with his implicit belief that his parents are always right, he must repress his natural feelings, for he is totally dependent upon his parents. They have got to be right. For many years such repressed feelings may lie smouldering with no outlet until that person becomes a parent themselves. Then they assume the position of power. Often quite unconsciously, they then proceed to do to their children the negative things that were done to them in their own childhood. The cycle repeats and repeats itself, with children being coerced into denying the existence of their own feelings in order to satisfy the emotional demands of their parents, then doing the same thing to their own children.

Reading *For Your Own Good* really brought home to me how Peter and I had passed on to Sam the product of our own unhappy childhoods; how two separate lines of accumulated emotional deprivation had merged with the birth of our son. Every page seemed to expose some new horror that related directly to us. No wonder I had shied away from reading this book. Now that I was doing so, my picture of autism was being filled in with colours harsh and clear.

14

SHIFTING SANDS

Not long after he moved away from home, Peter had given Sam an expensive bicycle. Since then the bicycle had sat in our garage, threatening to become yet another failed project. Sometimes Sam went to look at it, even to touch it, but that was as far as he went. Peter and I had both tried teaching him to cycle, but without success.

At various times I had taken Sam along the lane near our house, shouting for him to keep his feet on the pedals while I attempted to keep the bicycle upright. The problem as usual was getting Sam to focus his attention and energy upon the job in hand. I remember feeling that this would never happen, for whenever I passed the bike to Sam he would allow it to slip from his grasp and topple to the ground. He was so apathetic and I would get furious with him. I think the turning point came when one day after Sam had allowed the machine to crash to the ground I lost my temper.

'Pick up your bike and bring it home,' I shouted, walking back along the lane. To my surprise Sam did pick it up, and wheeled it along as he followed after me. After this I refused to pick up Sam's bike for him, or to manipulate it out of the gate, and he was forced to use his own muscle power. Once he had been persuaded to take responsibility for his bicycle in this way himself, learning how to ride it was fairly easy for him.

The dog-walkers along our lane soon came to know us well. They watched as Sam progressed from those first few wobbly yards to careering hair-raisingly from one end of the lane to the other. Occasionally an old lady would comment encouragingly upon his progress and this really cheered me.

Other people were less tolerant, but they all learned to leap aside when they saw Sam coming. By the time we had got to the point of Sam going off by himself I had bought a bicycle of my own, for he needed a minder. I saved many a group of walkers from decimation. 'Look out, Sam,' I would screech as he headed straight towards them. Once he had mastered actually riding his bicycle, Sam needed to learn how to take off. Our friend Jake was helpful here. Having been a teacher, Jake understood the importance of breaking a task down into small steps, and this was how he taught Sam to launch himself. He showed him how to lean the bike against the fence, then how to push himself off from this position, then eventually to put his weight on one pedal and take off from a standing position. At last Sam could ride his bike. I was proud of him. Not only had he mastered a difficult feat but he was controlling a machine by his own actions, and he was mobile. I felt sure that this was important to him in a symbolic sense as well as opening up practical possibilities.

Sam learning to ride his bicycle was in some ways a breakthrough in our relationship. It was marvellous knowing that he had learned how to do something, and sheer delight to see the happy confidence on his face as he rode off down the lane. It also meant that there was something that we could do together. Cycling behind Sam I experienced almost for the first time the joy of sharing an ordinary and involving activity with my child. In this situation at least, he looked just like any other boy of his age. Speeding down the lane with the air rushing past us and the smell of summer in the air I felt optimistic. Perhaps Sam would get better, perhaps he would learn to talk.

Sam's school report also sounded hopeful. Mrs Thompson wrote:

> On the whole his relationships outside the classroom have become much more secure. He still relates more with adults and very little with his peer group but it is a great improvement on the isolated little boy who first arrived.

Now that he had some reliable structures in his life – such as his psychotherapy, school, Lucy and his horseriding – Sam seemed to feel supported enough to begin taking a few small, tentative steps into the outside world. By this I mean that he sometimes allowed himself to manipulate objects (toys for example) and he would sometimes, very briefly, relate to other people. He touched the world, gingerly, and allowed it to touch him, but any amount of pressure caused him to withdraw like a sensitive plant.

The two aspects of Sam's behaviour that had always seemed to be the most accurate barometers of his anxiety level – and hence his ability to interact – were his play and his sleep pattern. Both were now better than they had ever been.

Sam's repertoire of play activities had increased. He amused himself occasionally with his cars and his roads, did jigsaw puzzles, and now and then put a few pieces of Lego together. Sometimes he played his harmonica, but usually this ended with him flinging it under the bed. Perhaps it reopened old wounds for Sam by reminding him of times when he and his father had played their harmonicas together in the bath. Quite often now Sam spent his evenings slotting together the pieces of his wooden train set – building bridges and tunnels to create a much more sophisticated construction than anything he had previously attempted. This was different from the old days, when I would sit watching the television and he would do little more than pick fluff from the carpet. I loved to see Sam playing in this way, but the jolt of surprise and pleasure that it gave me made me realize how little he had played. Eight and a half years of not playing, not learning, not experiencing the world in which we live – the idea was chilling.

Lucy had helped a great deal. During the two and a half years that she had been looking after Sam, Lucy had established a relationship with him from which he derived much security. She was level-headed, and she knew how to anticipate Sam's reactions and avert emotional upheavals. She was not afraid to take him down to the field where the other children played, and to act as a social support for him so that he could spend time amongst them. I am sure that Sam appreciated this, as he also did a particular incident that Lucy told me about. It happened during the school holidays. She and Sam had been out for the day and were just getting off a bus in the city centre. Sam's carrying object at that time was a small green metal van – a Matchbox toy – which he accidentally dropped as he stepped down from the bus. Sam was distraught. Lucy dived through the oncoming traffic, risking life and limb to retrieve Sam's van. Sam was delighted to have it back, even though it had been thoroughly flattened. He treasures it still – and cheerfully re-enacts the scene of the giant red bus squashing the little green van beneath its wheels.

Lucy had always managed to cope with Sam's behaviour, be it fearful, angry or isolated. But suddenly he started acting towards her in a way that she found difficult to handle. He began to taunt her – making noises at her in a sneering sort of way. Lucy found it very upsetting, but Sam had what must have seemed to him like a good reason for attacking her as he did. Lucy was leaving him. Sam is very perceptive, and although he had not been told that she was going, I am sure he knew through something that he had overheard. Like a normal child, only more so, Sam blamed himself for the pain caused him by the actions of others. This was why I wanted Lucy to tell him herself that she was leaving – to reassure him that it was for her own personal reasons and not because she did not like him any more. The days slipped by and still she said nothing. She probably found the idea of telling Sam too painful. Eventually I told him myself that Lucy had to go. He did not respond – he probably knew already. A few days later she left.

Lucy's departure meant that another person who was important to Sam had walked out of his life. I could not bear to think of him feeling rejected or lonely, but by now I realized that my anxiety regarding such things probably upset him more than the actual events, and so I tried hard to hide it.

Initially the effects of Lucy leaving were to some extent masked for Sam. I took time off work to look for a replacement childminder, which meant that for some weeks I was at home to meet him when he arrived back from school. Sam seemed to love this. He would rush from the taxi to the front door, then when he saw me waiting for him he would cover his face with his hands, only gradually allowing himself to peep through his fingers, then eventually to look briefly at me and smile. It was as though the experience was too intense to be borne in its natural state and had first of all to be filtered through his fingers. The difference between this sort of reunion and Sam's tense, rejecting behaviour when I used to arrive home from work only a year before was striking.

During that summer Sam and I went to stay near the coast for a week. I will never forget his reaction to the sea, which he had not seen for many years. As it appeared over the dunes he became wildly excited, running down the beach at full pelt, shedding his clothes as he went. By the time he got to the water's edge he was almost naked. Despite the chilly breeze Sam waded in. I sympathized with the intensity of his reaction for I also loved the sea, though I had forgotten just how much. Two hours later I dragged him out of the water, blue and shivering, but joyful. Having discovered something that we both liked to do, we swam in the sea as often as possible that summer.

After our holiday the problem of finding a replacement for Lucy became pressing. It was three years since I had been in the position of looking for somebody to take care of Sam and it was interesting to note the difference between the sort of person that I had searched for then and the one that I now hoped to find. Then I had wanted somebody solid and dependable, and Lucy was both of these things. Playfulness had seemed less important, for Sam needed security above everything, and he did not play much anyway. Now I toyed with the idea of getting a much younger person, perhaps a teenager whose exuberance might encourage Sam to communicate and entice him to play. I interviewed half a dozen young women but the right one was not easy to find, if indeed she existed at all. The girls that I saw all seemed either to have missed out on the vitality of youth, or to be too immature to cope with Sam's sometimes difficult behaviour.

Eventually my hand was forced by necessity and I engaged somebody who lived fairly close by in the hope that this would at least make practical arrangements comparatively easy. But things did not work out well between Cathy and Sam. Every night for weeks a scene of utter devastation greeted me on my arrival home from work. The broken pot plants, smashed crockery, and curtains down on the floor were sure signs that something was badly wrong. I was almost frantic trying to decide what to do, for the cause of Sam's disruptive behaviour was a mystery. It occurred to me that he might be missing Lucy. Perhaps the fact that she was not coming back had not really registered until the reality of her replacement confronted him. My going back to work could have upset him — he had got used to having me at home. Or maybe he did not like

Cathy for some reason. There was no way of knowing, for Sam told me nothing.

But whatever was wrong was upsetting Sam a great deal, for one day when he and Cathy were out walking, he gave her the slip. I arrived home to find a note saying that Sam was missing. Cathy and I searched the lane and the surrounding area for twenty minutes, then I telephoned the police. Darkness was falling as we paced up and down, waiting for the sniffer dogs to arrive. Thinking about Sam and worrying about what might have happened to him, I realized how much my feelings for him had changed. Several years before it might not have been true, but now I would be heartbroken if anything happened to my son. At last the news came through on our policeman's two-way radio – Sam had been found. He was wandering about on a golf course less than a mile away. He had been spotted by two boys whom the police had questioned. I heaved a sigh of relief. Sam was all right, apparently, but frightened; he would not allow the policeman to get anywhere near him. By the time I arrived at the scene the situation had changed. Sam had been coaxed into a police car, and was actually looking rather pleased with himself. He had obviously enjoyed the last part of his adventure at least. I just felt sick at the thought of the two major roads that he must have crossed between our house and where he eventually turned up.

Although I did not like the idea of Sam having yet another change in his life it seemed best that Cathy should leave as things were obviously not working out. After her departure I found somebody whom Sam really did seem to like. Sadly she became ill, and so she too had to leave after only a few months with us.

The year had started so well for Sam, but now it seemed to be dissolving into a nightmare of insecurity for him. Not only were his carers coming and going with monotonous regularity, but his friend Tim had left Springfield school. As with Lucy's departure, Sam did not seem particularly bothered when told that Tim was not coming back. But later when the truth had sunk in, he mourned the loss of his friend. It broke my heart to find Sam studying photographs of himself and Tim together. It seemed so unfair that his only friend should go away. Sam's loneliness weighed heavily upon me – I shuddered to think of how it must feel to him.

The disruptions during the latter part of our year were reflected in Sam's behaviour. The bedtime pattern that I thought was at last established just disappeared. I was back to broken nights, no evenings of my own, and feeling tired all the time. I suppose that I should have hung on tenaciously to our new routine, but my resolve was weakened by the various upheavals in our lives. Sam was again sitting halfway down the stairs, and calling me up every few minutes. I was exhausted and feeling desperate when help came from an unexpected quarter.

The headmaster of Springfield school, Mr Kirby, took his job seriously, which to him meant offering support and help to the families of his disturbed pupils if and when necessary. Sometimes he came to our house in the evening to discuss Sam's progress with me. On one such occasion Sam was in full sail, flinging things over the banisters and shouting to get me upstairs with him. My embarrassment was obvious, as was the fact that Sam had more control over the situation than I did. Mr Kirby gave me some practical advice. He said that I should insist that Sam stay in his bedroom, even if this meant going back to square one and sitting just outside until he went to sleep. The ground that I had previously gained had been lost by allowing Sam to leave his room at all once he had gone to bed, said Mr Kirby. I must therefore progress again by small steps to get back to where we had been, that is, with me downstairs and Sam in his bedroom. Consolidate your position, Mr Kirby told me, and do not backslide. It sounded like a battle plan, and a battle was how it felt. I did what Mr Kirby suggested, and did get Sam back into his bedroom again. And this time I did not let things slip.

Having re-established Sam's bedtime routine I wanted at all costs to avoid any more stress or upheaval, in the hope that we might regain the calm regularity of life as I remembered it being before Lucy had left. The idea of interviewing for another childminder seemed too awful, as did the thought of trying to persuade Sam that he could trust whoever came not to go away and leave him after a short time. Neither could I bear the thought of having to get used to yet another stranger in the house. Yet again, Sam's school came to my rescue. They agreed to let him have his evening meal with the boarders, then stay on at school until I could collect him on my way home from work. This made a long day for Sam, but it was the only solution that I could find to our problems at that time.

When we were together Sam was still obsessively dependent upon my physical presence and he still did not much like me even leaving the room. Perhaps because his father had gone, Lucy had gone and Tim had gone, Sam felt that I might go too. Or perhaps he felt that he could not rely upon me because of the unpredictability of my behaviour. Sometimes I felt optimistic and would sing and dance with Sam, which he loved; other days life weighed heavily upon me. Then I found it difficult to manage the practical aspects of day-to-day living and impossible to relate spontaneously to Sam. He must have wondered what he had done to make me switch off. He was continually preoccupied by my emotional state, hanging anxiously upon my every move to see which way we were heading next. One day I caught his look of worried concern in my driving mirror.

Sometimes I catch Sam watching me intently. He is looking for an angry, tense expression, but if I show him that I'm relaxed and in control, he relaxes too. He must worry about me a great deal. How dreadful. Last week he was sitting behind me in the back seat of the car when I saw his face in the mirror. He was leaning forward, watching me anxiously, unaware that I could see him. He was trying to catch a glimpse of my face as I turned to look out of the window. He looked so deeply worried – it really horrified me. This is not a look that I would normally see for his observations are usually surreptitious. He relaxed when I chatted and smiled at him.

I was appalled to see how much what I did affected Sam. My therapy was helping me to view my relationship with my son more objectively, and to temper the more destructive aspects of it, but understanding the problems did not provide the solutions. Balanced, sensible behaviour did not come naturally to me, but I was trying, and things were gradually improving between me and Sam. I longed to be able to give him what I now knew that he needed so badly – a calm, happy me, and a secure environment. It was ironic that the more I came to understand my son, the greater was my awareness of the shortfall between what was available to him and what he would need if he was to really start lowering his defences. I used to daydream about providing Sam with a network of supportive, caring people – a family, a therapist five times a week, a teacher all to himself. But as Frances Tustin often said to me, 'We do the best that we can.'

15

LANGUAGE AND
SYMBOLISM

While I do not pretend to understand the aims and methods of the many different types of psychotherapy that are available, my own experience has enabled me to form an impression of how at least some therapists work.

By encouraging clients to talk about their reactions to things that happen in everyday life, the therapist helps them to become conscious of their thoughts and feelings, and of the way in which they respond to the environment. The therapist may help her client to become more aware of what he is actually saying by repeating his own words back to him. Or she may make observations about his behaviour, commenting that he seems angry or upset. She may ask questions, or point out connections. In this way a person is helped to build up a picture of how he behaves and interacts with the world in which he lives. As previously unrecognizable or ill-defined patterns of behaviour become clearer during the course of therapy, awareness and understanding of the emotions that originally instigated the setting up of such patterns becomes possible.

Having psychotherapy myself did not make it any easier for me to imagine what actually happened between Sam and his therapist. Communication between the therapist and her client is, of course, usually by means of spoken language, but Sam used hardly any words. By his whole demeanour he rejected any approaches by other people. Knowing how isolated Sam was I wondered how on earth his therapist could make contact with him, let alone deduce anything about his inner thoughts or feelings; without doing so I did not understand how she could possibly help him.

Through my weekly feedback telephone conversations with

Frances Tustin I gradually formed an impression of what Lisa was doing with Sam. During the session she would concentrate her attention upon him – sort of 'holding' him in her mind – and try to 'read' his behaviour in order to elicit information about what was going on inside his head. She would then talk to him about what he was doing, and so through this verbal interpretation of his actions, she attempted to forge a link between herself and my son.

I knew that I was fortunate to have come across a psychotherapist with both the specialized skills and the inclination to tackle the daunting problems presented by a severely autistic child. Neither did I overlook the benefits that accrued from being in weekly contact with somebody as knowledgeable as Frances Tustin. At times I relied upon this contact to help me believe in the very existence of Sam as a person in his own right – a person who could be helped.

His personality was so often hidden from view behind his autistic mask, or was in such a state of disarray, that relating to him seemed almost impossible. When locked into an obsession he would emit a loud humming noise, making himself quite unreachable; when prey to explosive feelings he would throw himself and his toys about the room in a chaotic manner. Attempting to understand Sam when he was in either of these states was like peering through a thick fog, trying to make sense of a blurred, indefinable shape. Sometimes Mrs Tustin helped me to recognize that shape, and to distinguish its outline.

She explained to me how rampaging around the room destroying things was both frightening and harmful to Sam. She also explained that it is when left to deal with these explosive feelings alone that autistic children adopt the repressive strategies that are a barricade against their emotions. Sam needed help in learning how to manage his strong feelings, and how to express such feelings in a normal rather than pathological way. He needed to have his feelings received and understood, contained, organized and patterned, so that he would be less at the mercy of his uncontrolled impulsiveness.

Frances Tustin often reiterated the importance of talking to Sam about what was happening around him and about how he might be feeling. Although this is difficult for me, when I do manage it I am always struck by how much it seems to help Sam. For example, when Lucy stopped coming to look after him, I knew that he missed her, but he had no way of expressing how he felt. Sam never cried – he had not done so since he was a baby – and talking about how sad it was when people went away at least made his sadness seem safe and acceptable. Sam makes it quite obvious when I hit upon something that is bothering him as his face relaxes into a smile and he throws his arms around my neck. Experiencing the sharing of feelings that so many people take for granted must provide a joyful release for him.

Bringing things into the open like this also helps to loosen the vice-like grip in which Sam and I still seem to hold each other at times, though this happens less often now. Our relationship is changing – I can feel it happening. I can not easily pinpoint just how things have altered, especially as the lines of communication between Sam and myself wax and wane like shadows being thrown into hard focus, then suddenly disappearing when the light is obliterated. But the bond between us is growing. It is strengthening in a more healthy way, which allows for some individual freedom for each of us. When I first began to notice this change it seemed quite miraculous. There was a feeling of being 'with' somebody else, a feeling that I was no longer alone when Sam was with me. This awareness of another presence struck me quite forcefully the first few times when I noticed it. It was new, and different from the old feeling of being isolated yet controlled by an almost alien power.

Sometimes Sam and I now actually seem able to communicate with each other, which is marvellous, but I am still aware that the exclusive relationship between us does not foster the development of his language. He has only to say a single word (with very poor pronunciation) for me to know exactly what he means. He uses a sort of verbal shorthand, and probably does not see the point of using a sentence when a word seems to serve just as well. For example, when I collect him from school I am greeted with a frantic 'Dow, dow, dow'. What Sam means is, 'Can I come downstairs after my bath?'

If I respond with, 'Do you mean that you want to come downstairs?' he is not satisfied, because the sentence is not complete, as far as he is concerned. He will say, 'Bah, bah,' peering anxiously into my face.

'Do you mean that you want to come downstairs after your bath?' I obligingly complete the sentence to Sam's satisfaction.

'Yeh,' he will say. Then when I have answered, 'Yes, you can come down after your bath,' he will smile, relax and move on to something else.

I am always so pleased when Sam makes any attempt to communicate verbally that I cannot resist first of all working out what he is saying, and then responding to it in the way that he wants me to. I sometimes feel as though he is teaching me to understand his language, rather than him learning to speak mine. He and I are still too close. I understand him too well. Nevertheless it is only since the lines of communication have begun to open up between us that he has started showing a real desire to contact other people. And so I attempt to negotiate a fine balance between responding positively to what Sam does say, and insisting upon better pronunciation and more explicit speech.

Going back to the very beginning, it is possible to trace the pattern of Sam's attempts to communicate. Between eight and nine months he babbled in the normal manner. At that time I wrote down some of the sounds that he used to make – 'Bem, meb, ba ba, da da.' I do not know whether Sam vocalized more or less than any other child, but I do recall an occasion during his ninth month when a visitor meeting him for the first time told me that he would definitely talk early. He was gregarious that day, and very loquacious.

But Sam did not progress in the normal manner from babbling to naming a whole variety of objects, although he did acquire a few words in his second year. 'Tractor' was his first – 'Da-haw' he would shout in a loud joyful voice whenever he saw one. Also 'bah' (bath), 'tar' (star), 'da' (dog), and half a dozen or so others.

The single words that Sam used as labels when he was about two years old did not increase much during his third and fourth years. In fact the occasional addition of a new word would as often as not be countered by the dropping of an old one from his vocabulary.

Although Sam did have some speech therapy at this time I think it actually did him more harm than good. He hated going, and the speech therapist seemed not to have the vaguest notion of how to deal with him. She would sit at the table naming objects, and he would either turn the other way, sometimes making a strangled choking noise, or else staring vacantly at the wall behind her.

Sam's development seemed almost to have ceased during these dark years. His only way of communicating his desires was by moving my hand towards whatever it was that he wanted. He expressed his turbulent inner feelings by throwing things, or by kicking and shouting to be picked up and then immediately wanting to get down again. Large amounts of his time were spent indulging in repetitive, isolating activities. And yet looking back I can see that he made quite definite statements regarding some of his feelings. For example, the way that Sam would push Peter and I together and attempt to join our hands, or carefully place my hand on the arm of his teacher, seemed obvious indications that he wanted the relevant adults in his life to join forces and pull together.

One of the few signs that Sam's psychologist did consider hopeful in those early days was the fact that Sam seemed able to generalize. Once he knew the name of an object he could identify its significant features and extend his understanding to include all objects with those features in the same category. He clearly realized that a table was not just that thing in our kitchen, it was any horizontal surface supported by legs, at which you could sit and do things. I noted how interested Sam was in classifying objects when he was about three and a half.

Sam seems happy this morning, doing lots of matching. As soon as he comes across an object he goes to fetch a replica (a picture, small toy version etc). Sometimes he collects three or four versions of the object, and seems to derive great satisfaction from doing this.

It was not until we started holding therapy that I began to think of Sam's behaviour as being connected with the way he felt. Becoming aware of his violent emotions – as opposed to almost succeeding in denying their existence – made me see that Sam was an undeniably real person. This shift in attitude brought with it the awareness that Sam must understand at least some of what he heard, and over a period of time this affected the way that I spoke to him.

In fact the first step was when I started speaking to him at all – for many years he had seemed strangely non-existent in his unreachable state.

Although during the next few years Sam's understanding increased a great deal (or perhaps it was just my appreciation of it), his vocabulary of spoken words seemed hardly to alter. He still named objects only occasionally, and replied to questions with a one-word answer if at all.

Not until Sam's seventh year did I begin to learn anything about him from what he was saying. I remember the very first time that he told me something. He came to me in the garden, held up his hand and said, 'Hurt.' I was astonished, and overjoyed. My son had come to me for help – I felt ten feet tall. He did indeed have a small scratch on his finger, which I bathed and tended as if it was a gaping wound.

When Sam did start to communicate his feelings in this way, the messages he gave were highly emotive. His preoccupation with the idea of being injured was obvious. He was acutely concerned about the multifarious dangers that might befall him, and much enamoured of ambulances which perhaps he felt came to the rescue when disaster struck. The sound of a distant siren would cause a frenzy of excitement, and an enormous effort on Sam's part to get to the revered object or to a position from which he could see it. 'A-be-la,' he would repeat, over and over. I assumed that he had picked up the fact that ambulances transport sick people to the hospital, which was Sam's other great love at that time. 'Pital' (hospital), he would say, if a cup or glass was dropped. What he meant was that the pieces of broken glass might cut him, and make it necessary for him to go to the hospital. He soon began to anticipate this danger even before any accident occurred – at one point the number and variety of objects that Sam considered potentially harmful seemed to be almost without limit. A plethora of 'pital's was evoked by such innocuous items as a ladder or roof (he could fall from them), a window (it might break and cut him), a knife spied on the draining board, cars on the road (they might crash into him, which he indicated by thumping his chest, saying 'Cra, pital').

Sometimes he made his fears regarding sharp objects even more explicit. With his fingertips bunched together he would make a wild spurting gesture, arching out from his throat or arm. 'Bluh-ow' (blood out), he would cry dramatically, acting out the imagined consequences of such an object cutting him. Then about six months later the possibly final result of such frightening events occurred to him. 'Dead,' he would say in tragic tones, his face assuming an expression of high melodrama. 'Cra, dead.'

To me it seems impossible not to equate Sam's obvious concern about physical danger with his own very real fears regarding the psychological risk that he takes in lowering his defences. From his point of view being locked in his autistic shell is safe, despite the emotional impoverishment, boredom and loneliness. So while part of him strives to communicate with other people and to learn about the world in which he lives, the more in touch he becomes with this world, the more he perceives the dangers (both physical and psychological) that are part of everyday life.

Perhaps Sam feels ambivalent about having a direct line of communication between himself and other people or perhaps he cannot see the point of exerting himself when he manages well enough without speech, but for whatever reason, his speech remains almost indecipherable. Only two or three adults are able to understand anything that he says; most other people fail to recognize that he talks at all and therefore assume that he does not understand what is being said either. Yet the content of Sam's thought as reflected in the minimal amount of speech that he does have has altered over the past couple of years. Out of his preoccupation with dangerous objects and how they might hurt him has grown Sam's interest in things that he perceives as powerful.

Like many children he has always liked big machines, but when he came across tube trains they seemed to strike a special chord. I shall never forget those first dozen or so journeys during which he sat beside me, wide eyed and shaking with excitement. Apprehension, amazement, fear and admiration flitted across Sam's face as the carriages rattled and roared through the tunnels. From where we stood on the platform he would peer into the darkness, awe-struck by the subterranean world, but especially so by the enormous trains that came crashing towards him.

Now Sam is a seasoned traveller and has become somewhat blasé about the London underground, but those first few encounters with the thundering metal monsters had a profound effect upon him. He soon started saying 'du-day' (tube train), although it took me some weeks to work this out. When I did eventually decipher his meaning Sam was delighted. 'Du-day, du-day,' he would shout, 'Lu-dle' (London).

It soon became apparent that to Sam 'tube train' represented far more than just a tube train. The first time he applied the words to me I was puzzled. Surely my son knew the difference between his mother and a tube train? Then by noting the context in which he said this, I began to understand what Sam meant. He would call me a tube train when he felt that I had performed well in some way. For example, if I protected him when he felt threatened, or if I spoke up in defence of his ability to understand when somebody was talking about him – then he would see me as a strong and powerful person. He would point to me, smiling coyly, and whisper 'Du-day.' His meaning was unmistakable.

He did not do it often, but when Sam attributed the power of one of his great machines to me, I was deeply flattered. Within a few months tube train had been replaced by 'Concorde'. It seemed that an object came to symbolize power for Sam when he had been particularly impressed by its supreme strength and energy. Concorde did occasionally come to the airport near where we lived, but Sam's use of the word dated from a particular day when we had both looked up into the sky to see the enormous bird-like machine flying unexpectedly low just above us. 'Cong-caw,' said Sam, his eyes like saucers. Concorde made its mark that day and was never forgotten.

One morning soon after this a friend called by, wanting to talk to me about some work he was doing. I was in the middle of a game with Sam. 'I'm busy with Sam at the moment,' I told my friend. 'Come back later.' He was annoyed, but Sam was delighted. As I closed the door – feeling guilty – Sam came up to me. 'Cong-caw,' he said, his hand gently touching my arm. His face wore the merest suggestion of a smile – for a second his eyes met mine. I knew that I had done the right thing. My heart swelled with pride, for both Sam and myself, but how I longed to have just a small part of the strength that Sam attributed to me on these rare occasions.

At about this time Sam became enamoured of a whole range

of power tools – drills, cleaners, saws. He was thrilled by the chainsaw that our neighbour used to chop wood each weekend, and was torn between wanting to be near the gnawing monster and his terror of it. At the first hint of its raucous tones he would race to the scene, only to run to and from it in a state of conflicting emotions. Eventually he would compromise, and settle upon a safe distance from which to observe, usually from behind a tree.

Sam remains interested in things that symbolize power for him, but his observations of the world are gradually becoming more subtle. Those big, strong, noisy objects made their presence felt in an obvious sort of way, but from them Sam has moved on to more abstract variations on the theme of power. He has, for instance, become fascinated by electricity pylons and poles. During our walks across the fields he likes to follow the same route as the pylons that stride over the hillsides. When we approach the foot of one of these huge structures Sam gets very excited, and will fight his way through undergrowth if necessary in order to touch the revered object. 'Pye-luh,' Sam will say, looking at me with a rapt expression upon his face. 'Tuh pye-luh' (touch pylon). And he does, with one tentative finger. Perhaps he feels that the power will flow into him.

At first I thought that Sam's devotion to pylons and poles might be simply because of the way in which they loom large and imposing against the landscape. But it soon became apparent that there was more to it than that. Sam knew that flicking a switch made things happen (like a light or a television come on), and he also knew that the linking device between the event and the switch was the 'wi-ya' (wire). He had noticed that the great pylons and smaller poles had wires coming from them, and so perhaps assumed that the power flowed from them, down along the wires to the scene of the action. Apart from his misconception concerning the generation of power, Sam's deductions were of course correct.

During these walks of ours I often have cause to think about Sam's primitive way of viewing the world. I am always struck by the similarity between his apparent idolization of an object which to him seems either powerful or a source of power (I'm not sure which), and the more primitive forms of worship that human beings have used in the past and in some cultures continue to use.

Sam's thought processes are still rigid and narrow. They are cramped by fear. His tentative observations reveal a world in which the flow of events must seem to be impelled by mysterious forces. They are forces beyond Sam's comprehension, for he does not have a proper sense of his own identity and cannot therefore see beyond himself. He feels himself to be utterly powerless.

Sam explains the unexplainable in the same way that human beings have always done so – by creating gods. More recently I am pleased to notice that he has started idolizing real people as well as inanimate objects. For example, the headmaster of his school, Mr Kirby, seems to inspire Sam with great awe, perhaps because he looms large as both a figure of authority and an important male influence in Sam's life. Sam is intrigued by Mr Kirby's house, which is in the school grounds. As we drive past he cranes his neck to look inside, yet when Mr Kirby offered to take him there one day, Sam ran away and hid. Fear overcame his curiosity.

Sam is convinced that Mr Kirby has a pylon in his house. 'Pye-luh Car-gee how' (pylon Kirby's house), he informs me excitedly, pointing as we go past. How else to explain such incredible powers as those that Mr Kirby obviously possesses? School is a large proportion of Sam's life, and this man seems to control it all. He towers above Sam in the assembly hall (Mr Kirby is a tall man) and he shapes the future. Mr Kirby says that things will happen, and they do happen. He must certainly have a pylon somewhere!

Sam's total preoccupation with his subject is well illustrated by an incident a year or two ago. He was quite keen on music at the time and as we listened to one of his tapes he was examining the recorder and speakers. When I asked Sam what was coming out of the speakers I was expecting him to answer 'Music'. But no. 'Wires,' he said. The fact that electricity wires have substance while music is ephemeral could be seen as the explanation for Sam's literal answer to my question, but with a slight shift of focus Sam's reply can be explained in a different way altogether. The wires that trailed out of the back of the speaker were to Sam far more important than the music, even though he liked the music, for the wires carried the magic substance that made things happen. The music was merely pleasurable; the wires carried the mysterious life-force that so fascinated Sam, perhaps because he felt himself to be involved in a constant battle to survive.

Even now Sam retains his interest in electricity wires and the route that they follow. He is aware that they are buried beneath the ground, and whenever we visit a new place, he will look to me and enquire, 'Wi-ya uddu road?' (Wire under road?)

Sam's mind is undeveloped and his thinking abilities are at this stage limited, yet within the narrow confines of his selected areas of interest, he continues to broaden his horizons. Fascination with power has led on to an interest in motors. It would be a big step forward for Sam if he got to the point of wanting to know how they actually worked – at the moment his concern extends only to whether an object has one or not.

When Sam first began to mention motors it took me some time to decipher his meaning. I could not understand what he was saying with 'Car-key bow-uh,' but he helped me by forming the shapes with his fingers. First he made a rectangle – which turned out to be a castle – then he formed a circle from his finger and thumb, which I came to learn represented a motor. He was referring to a large inflatable castle with an accompanying motor which, unbeknown to me, had been erected in the school grounds. Sam had seen the castle being deflated after the motor had been turned off (in fact I think that the motor served only to cool the circulating air), and had obviously been greatly impressed by the spectacle.

Recently Sam's hero worship has become even more rooted in the real world. He has decided that he likes Michael Jackson. The music has a heavy beat and an easily identifiable rhythm. Sam plays it over and over on his personal stereo, headphones clamped to his ears, his eyes upon some distant point, his face intent. My attention was drawn to Sam's interest when he was rummaging through our tapes one day, obviously looking for something. He had been saying 'Bang bang', and looking at me expectantly for the past week or two. Now I suddenly understood what he meant. 'Bang bang' referred to the beat of the music – he wanted to listen to Michael Jackson. When we found the tape Sam leapt up in great excitement. 'Ja-uh,' he said, 'bang bang.' This was indeed bang bang music. Whenever Michael Jackson appeared on the television thereafter, Sam would be glued to the set.

He is still keen on 'Ja-uh' and has on several occasions dragged me through the streets in pursuit of a person who happens to resemble his idol. I am pleased by Sam's enthusiasm for a pop singer – it seems like a distinct improvement on worshipping an electricity pylon (although he still does that as well). Sitting gazing at the television in rapt attention seems so normal – the sort of thing that any nine-year-old might do. But because I see Sam's veneration in the context of a series of preoccupations with 'powerful' objects and people it somehow seems different from that of an ordinary child. Perhaps, however, the difference is not so great after all.

It is difficult to understand in any detail how Sam thinks because he has so little language. Two or three words are used to convey an idea in a way that nobody who does not know him could possibly understand. His pronunciation is still so poor that many words are unrecognizable. Normally he articulates only the first consonant and vowel sound, and never a final consonant. Sometimes he will not even bother to do this, but will simply reproduce the rhythm of a word. To understand Sam it is necessary to interpret the sense of what he is saying from the context in which he speaks, and apart from myself and his teacher, few people have either the time or the inclination to do this.

Sam and I may communicate via a secret language, but at least I am now beginning to gain some insight into what goes on in my son's mind. Between us there is evolving a small amount of common ground – an area of shared understanding. When Sam speaks of his pylons and wires and bang bang music I usually know what he means and am therefore able to respond to him. We can have a conversation, albeit primitive and lopsided.

I first noticed that there was some dialogue developing between the two of us at about the same time as Sam started going with his class to a children's soft play area once a week. He loved this event, which consisted of much wild leaping about and jumping into a pool filled with foam balls. Sam became obsessed by the 'play-air-ear' (play area), and even made a simple model of it out of Duplo. The play area seemed to represent something very significant for him. It was like a sort of 'living area' – a small space in Sam's week in which he could really let go if he wanted to, and during which he was released from the iron grip that normally held his emotions in check. In metaphorical terms the soft play area was for Sam a small arena in which it was safe to play, and this in turn was like the small pool of shared experience that was beginning to exist between him and myself.

Through Sam's slowly developing language I have come to understand his almost total preoccupation with the ideas of danger and power. He repeats the single words or short phrases that he uses concerning his chosen subjects over and over again. But Sam is also becoming more in touch with the world in a way that is not easy to define. It is as though a small part of his mind is freeing itself from the control exerted by his obsessional interests. One thing that he does now is to query future events – he likes to know exactly what is going to happen, and when. He has started showing a more detailed knowledge of what goes on around him. The broad terms in which he used to categorize objects are becoming more refined. As his awareness of opposites develops (big and little, good and bad), Sam is learning to cope with the grey area that comprises the space between two extremes. His attention span is increasing and he is learning to accommodate the fact that things are not always either perfect or useless. He is learning how to wait.

Sam's areas of interest are diversifying, yet I can still discern three distinct themes in the language that he has developed during the past nine and a half years. As well as his preoccupation with things that might hurt him and with different aspects of power, Sam is becoming more consciously aware of his own particular vulnerability in the face of danger, and so of the need to shield himself. He is showing that he no longer wants to be completely isolated, and is seeking some sort of less crippling protective device to replace his invisible wall. As this idea becomes woven into the fabric of his thoughts, the psychological cutting off that used to be Sam's automatic response to most things has assumed a physical form. Perhaps he is building a physical model as a way of trying to understand what it is that isolates him from other human beings.

This process began with Sam becoming fixated upon the idea of barriers. For many months he seemed to be constantly trying to define exactly what constituted a barrier by checking with me regarding each new fence, wall, set of railings, hedge or low structure that we came across. He also used to carry a piece of toy fencing with him when he went out, especially if it was to somewhere that he found slightly daunting. Perhaps it represented something that he could hide behind – a physical version of the protective psychological barrier that had been his autistic defence. I felt this to be a step forward, for at least Sam was acknowledging the existence of a barrier and consciously manipulating it.

In the same vein, Sam has developed an anxious concern regarding plasters. Like many small children he will sometimes ask for a plaster to cover a scratch, but for Sam the procedure of applying the plaster is riddled with conflict. He wants the plaster, but as soon as it has been stuck down he become desperate to have it removed. No sooner is it off than he wants it back on again. This situation causes him much distress, for he cannot decide whether he wants his hurt to be covered over or left exposed. The routine has now evolved to the point where Sam and I have a ritualized exchange, and so avoid the necessity of him acting out his conflict. 'Cut, cut,' Sam will say dramatically. 'Oh dear. I wonder whether it needs a plaster,' I reply. 'No, no,' he cries desperately. 'No, it doesn't need a plaster,' say I, 'it will get better soon.' Then Sam smiles and relaxes.

Sam's awareness of his vulnerability has manifested itself in many different ways. One of these is his recently acquired aversion to eating in public. When we are at home he choses to dine alone, but when there are other people present Sam insists on covering his head while he eats. In the café where we have lunch each Monday he puts an arm over his head and eats his meal with one hand; on the train going back he arouses the interest of other passengers by sitting under his jacket while he eats his crisps.

I had not really thought much about Sam's early eating problems until he started being difficult at mealtimes about two years ago. He began to taunt me – threatening to throw his dinner on the floor and behaving in a generally unruly manner. 'Didder law' (dinner floor), he would shout, tapping it towards the edge of the table while I sat embarrassed and furious across the table from him. Then after about six months of creating this nightmare mealtime situation, Sam changed from the disruptive child who threw his weight (and sometimes his food) around, to the little boy who cowered fearfully beneath his arm while he ate.

As Sam becomes more in touch with the world so his vulnerability increases, for behind his autistic screen are the painful experiences of his past. Sometimes now he feels that pain, and bears it, rather than retreating in the way that he used to. Recently I found him sitting on the floor, holding a picture of himself with his father. 'Bukkah' (broken), he said. 'Bukkah, bukkah.' His father was gone, their relationship was broken. His voice itself sounded lost and fractured – it filled me with an ineffable sadness.

I admire Sam when I see him trying to cope with his feelings and during his last holiday an incident impressed me. We were having a day out with a friend and her two children – a visit to a beautiful part of the Yorkshire Dales called Bolton Abbey – and had followed the nature trail that ran along the steep banks of a river before sitting for an hour or so gazing at the waterfall. Sam appeared to have enjoyed the day – he was calm and relaxed. For some weeks past he had been unhappy about wearing his shoes – constantly fastening and unfastening the velcro flap. When we got up to walk back from the waterfall Sam removed his shoes and refused to put them back on again. He was quite adamant; he did not want to wear them, even though the ground was covered in pebbles and farther up the slope with sharp rocky outcrops.

I was reminded of the many occasions on which Sam had decided to confront head on something which he found difficult. But this time it was different. He did not work himself into his usual state – pulling his shoes on and off in a frenzy of conflicting desires – but calmly took my arm and made it quite clear that he would require my help for the road ahead. Our progress along the rough track was slow and halting. As we struggled along the rutted path, Sam leaned upon me like a little old man. I wondered whether he saw the incident as I did. To me it seemed that he might be making a link between his unprotected feet and his exposed feelings, and that his determination to walk barefoot symbolized his desire to shed his protective cloak of autism, despite the pain involved. I could not be sure of my son's feelings, but whatever his thoughts at that time, he was at last beginning to acknowledge the fact that he wanted and needed my help. Sam was taking tentative steps into the land of the living, and I was delighted.

16

TEACHING AND LEARNING

The progress that Sam and I have made over the years sometimes seems like a series of steps. The space between those steps is filled by a set of smaller steps, and between those, smaller steps still. The most obvious changes are those that effect our daily lives, like Sam learning to go to bed on his own. The gradually increasing communication between us is less easy to quantify. Beyond my observations are the internal changes that must underlie the improvements that I can actually see in my son's behaviour.

Perhaps we will eventually be able to explain scientifically how children develop. A child's relations with his mother might become comprehensible in terms of chemical interactions. But whether we are examining brain cells under a microscope, observing isolated segments of behaviour, or studying the inherent patterns in the broad sweep of an individual's behaviour during his lifetime, our aim is till to identify how and why we think and act as we do. Within the wide spectrum of human behaviour there is enormous scope for conjecture about the way in which our minds function. Consequently there are many opposing views on the subject. These may turn out to be no more than different perspectives, and the different models that we have constructed in our attempts to understand our thought process may all be found to have a place when the picture that we are making of ourselves is complete.

At the moment that picture seems to me like an unfinished painting – patchy, and uneven in texture. Some parts are clearly drawn, even brightly coloured. Others are marked out in a crude form only. In some places the canvas remains completely blank. The overall effect is of striking contrast between the highlighted areas and the empty spaces between them. Not until the gaps are filled will the apparently unrelated pieces of the picture appear as part of an integrated whole.

Because of my experience with Sam I have read and thought a great deal about autism. I have found that ideas concerning human behaviour in general and autism in particular, often conflict with one another. Personally, I agree with people who explain the condition from which children like my son suffer as a defensive response to an unsympathetic environment. But I can appreciate why other people find it hard to believe that autism is related to external influences, especially when that environment does not seem to exert undue pressures upon particular children. A child may appear to have everything he could possibly need, including parents who seem devoted. But the stress to which autistic children are subjected can be far from obvious – for often both they and their parents are quite unconscious of the undercurrents within their relationship. A mother may not even realize that she stiffens each time she holds her baby, and may become confused and depressed when she notices his consequent withdrawal from her. Nor is it easy to spot the conflicting demands that are sometimes made upon a child, which make it impossible for him to negotiate a course of action. What can a child do if he finds that his crying (which is his only means of asking for the food he needs to stay alive) results in angry rejection and the loss of his mother's approval (which he also needs to survive)? I have watched parents unwittingly trap their children in such 'no win' situations, saddened by the knowledge that I have frequently done the same thing myself.

I think that Sam was an intelligent and responsive baby, and was therefore more likely to react to stressful situations by withdrawing from them. During those early months he responded in an extreme manner to his surroundings – quivering all over at the sight of something that he liked and covering his eyes and ears to exclude sights and sounds that were too much for him to cope with. Sam seemed to be acutely sensitive. Perhaps such sensitivity allows a child to make rapid and diverse mental connections, but also makes him vulnerable. His increased responsiveness would mean that pain, when he experienced it, was extreme too.

Sam and I have spent much of our lives together in actively

cutting off from each other. Although I can only conjecture regarding Sam's reasons for doing so, I know that I have avoided confronting my feelings about him because they involved guilt, fear, anger and pain. But in suppressing the feelings that relating to my son aroused in me, I made it difficult for myself to relate to him at all.

I have been called perverse and masochistic because I believe that Sam's autism is related to our relationship. But as far as I can see, it is the only explanation able to account for the apparently unrelated distortions in his behaviour. Although such thoughts are very upsetting, they are for me preferable to the heavy burden of pointless guilt or the deadness of being divorced from my emotions. I have found that reaching some understanding of how and why things happened as they did for Peter, Sam and myself has made for a better and a more open life for me and Sam, as well as freeing me to think about his condition more objectively.

I think that it is helpful to consider autism as having two quite distinct aspects – the cutting-off strategies that autistic children use and the accumulated retardation of learning that results from these strategies.

The cutting-off behaviour employed by children like Sam, such as indulging in obsessive activities, making repetitive noises and assuming deafness or failure to understand, make it extremely difficult to contact or communicate with them. Trying to speak through a wall of sound or attract the attention of somebody who is staring fixedly at a tiny object is almost impossible. This behaviour seems to be an automatic response to the need that autistic children have to escape, and is not under their conscious control. From my personal experience with Sam, I have concluded that the degree to which he is out of touch with his environment is closely associated with the level of anxiety from which he is suffering at any given time. Perhaps his cutting off is a safety valve, a way of avoiding intolerable levels of anxiety. If this is so then the only way of helping him is to alleviate the need to cut off by first of all determining and then removing the cause of his anxiety. I believe that this in turn is affected by a vast array of phenomena, including his feelings about his physical environment and the other people who are present, verbal communications that are being directed at him, and implicit communications, such as those conveyed by tone of voice and body language, which may conflict with what is actually being said.

Sam's continued use of cutting-off behaviour means that he has been, and remains, isolated for much of the time. As a consequence he has few opportunities for learning. Sam does not make much contact either with other people or with objects about him. To a large extent he is detached from his own thought processes. This degree of psychological isolation precludes the development of even basic concept formation, and so his overall development is severely retarded.

These two aspects of autism are, of course, considerations of the particular and the general situation – that which is happening at any given time, which is the anxious or isolating behaviour, and the accumulation of the results of the former, which is the general retardation. It is often difficult to disentangle one from the other. For example, Sam's anxiety prevents him from communicating with other people. This makes him vulnerable, which in turn makes him more anxious. In order to cope, he cuts himself off from his emotions. Then he suffers less from anxiety, but he gains nothing either. So as well as standing between him and other people, Sam's anxiety prevents him from accumulating the knowledge and experience that would help him to feel less vulnerable, and so less anxious.

I have often felt utterly lost in the maze of my attempts to understand my son's behaviour and the way in which he and I relate to each other. From the time during his fourth year when I first began really to think about his condition I have felt that he was both reachable and teachable. I felt that theoretically it must be possible to control Sam's environment absolutely, and therefore his responses to it. But considering the myriad phenomena that influence any human being at any given moment, the task seemed daunting, even impossible. I felt as though I was standing on top of a mountain, looking across to another summit on which I wanted to be. It looked so close, but between me and my destination lay a void. There was no tangled jungle through which to hack a path, no swirling river to cross, no rocky landscape over which to plot a course – nothing but a vast intangible emptiness. This feeling became familiar when I first started thinking about forging a relationshop with my son. To do so seemed impossible. We were both so isolated, so locked inside ourselves, and I had no experience of a good relationship upon which to draw.

I tried for years to structure situations between Sam and myself in order to teach him things, but my efforts always seemed to flounder. Frustration would overwhelm me when he rejected my attempts to communicate with him or when he went limp as I tried to get him to copy simple actions. At nearly eight years of age Sam could still barely be persuaded to hold a pencil, let alone learn to write.

When Sam learned to ride his bicycle it was the first time that I had ever felt instrumental in helping him to acquire a skill. I wondered whether I might be able to use the same procedure of working through a series of small steps for teaching him other things. Perhaps we had succeeded because there was somebody else involved – my friend Jake had sometimes given me an injection of hope when I felt flattened by Sam's apathy. Perhaps also it was easier to teach Sam things that provided us both with a physical outlet when frustration built up in the teaching situation.

I had always been enthusiastic about the idea of Sam learning to swim. Being taught to do so myself as a young child had helped me to gain confidence and since then I had always felt relaxed in water. Going to the pool was something that both Sam and I liked doing, but despite my efforts and Sam's obvious enjoyment, he refused to attempt to do the actual strokes. He would not hold his body in a horizontal position, and whenever I tried to hold him or draw his limbs through the proper movements, his muscles would go completely flaccid. In the end I would give up and just let him play about in the pool, which he loved.

I have watched Sam's confidence grow when he is in the water. I remember several years ago the frustration of watching him confront his fear as he tried to force himself to jump into the pool. For half an hour at a time he would stand on the edge making as if to jump, tensing and untensing his body, contorting his face with the agony of conflicting desires. If he could not bring himself to leap he would become very upset – then it was time for us to go. After months of battling with his fear Sam did get to the point where he would jump in from the side quite easily, and even down to the bottom of the pool to fetch his toy car. He seemed more relaxed in the water than out of it, and I felt sure that this was related to the fact that he and I were sharing a situation in which I felt relaxed.

But still Sam could not swim. What was needed was an expert, I decided. One of the instructors at our local baths agreed to take him on. I watched nervously from a distance as the instructor gradually lost confidence in the fact that he was being understood by Sam, who flopped helplessly, apparently in danger of drowning. After half an hour or so Mr Green was beaten, and sceptical of my assurances that Sam understood what was being said to him. At first I felt disappointed that yet another project seemed to have failed, then somewhat disoriented at finding myself in the teaching role, trying to explain to Mr Green how Sam was capable of more than he showed. Mr Green suggested that I was better equipped to teach Sam than he was, but said that he would do what he could to help. He watched as I persuaded Sam to do his 'arms only' dog paddle, more a sort of treading water. I tried harder than usual with Sam, partly in order to prove my claims regarding his comprehension and ability but also because I felt supported by Mr Green's interest. By the end of a long and intensive session during which Mr Green had intervened and helped with suggestions, I could see a huge improvement in what Sam was doing. This gave me confidence, and I was determined that I would teach him how to swim. We went to the baths every week after that and I pushed Sam hard. He learned how to swim in about three months.

Sam's progress delighted me. His achievement seemed a great bonus – I suppose that after nine years I had come to expect very little of him. Even the fact that he could neither speak, nor read, nor write, appeared to worry me less than it had previously done, but when an acquaintance expressed surprise and horror that Sam could not write I was shocked into taking a long hard look at the situation. At school he would make a poor copy of the letters of his name, but there were only three of these, and they were the only letters that he knew. At home he would not even do this. Sam's teacher did spend some time with him on a one-to-one basis, but her time was limited. Like so many schools, Springfield was understaffed. I saw that if Sam was to progress in this area he would need my help.

My previous attempts at teaching Sam to write – and there had been many of them – had all ended in failure. However hard I tried with him we seemed to become inevitably locked into a resentful stalemate. When I read about a feeling which therapists have to cope with – a drifting away and cutting off from their patients – it sounded familiar. This is apparently a response to a feeling of impotence which can occur when dealing with a person who is putting up massive psychological barriers. The would-be helper feels excluded, helpless and hopeless. The description fitted exactly the way that I had so often felt when trying to teach Sam something.

Armed with this knowledge and the experience of Sam's success with cycling and swimming, I decided to have another try at teaching him to write. Most days we do fifteen minutes or so of 'rah-dee' (writing). We started with lines and lines of 'm' joined up to make a continuous flow. Then we moved on to the upside-down version – lines of joined up 'u'. I began to introduce odd letters – after six months or so Sam knew most of the alphabet. He had less trouble memorizing the shapes than with some other aspects of writing. Changing from one letter to another, for example, was a problem. Once Sam has started writing a particular letter he prefers to lock himself into the security of repetition, and to continue doing so *ad infinitum*. What he most likes is to do this 'm' shape over and over, line after line. 'Var-duh' (viaduct), he calls it. 'Var-duh, var-duh,' says Sam, smiling wickedly at me as he launches himself into an orgy of 'm' shapes. Watching me out of the corner of his eye, he waits for me to say, 'Come on Sam let's do some words.' Then he makes a show of being upset, but in fact he has now learned to cope with changing from one letter to another. He has also learned that letters group together to make words, though he seemed to find this difficult. He now copies words, and is learning to write a few short ones from memory.

I think that Sam has done extremely well. In less than a year he has progressed from only just holding a pencil (this at least was the situation at home) to writing a word from memory. My son is not unintelligent, but his intelligence is buried deep.

One of the most important things when I am trying to teach Sam, and yet one of the most difficult for me, is to remain cheerful and consistent in my dealings with him. I sometimes find it hard to be optimistic, and to hold on to the positive thread of our relationship by remembering the good times that we have together. It is much easier to lose track of the progress that we have made, and to slip again into despair.

Living with Sam can be very disorienting – it is almost as though he exerts a strong pull towards chaos. While seemingly quite responsive and teachable at some times, he can at others be like an alien with whom there are no points of contact at all. The degree to which he is in touch fluctuates in a most tantalizing manner, and this is one reason why it is difficult to measure his progress in any formal sort of way. However I do note things that strike me as relevant or interesting. The following was written only a few months ago – six months or so after we had begun our 'rah-dee' sessions.

I've been trying to help Sam to draw diagonal lines today. He seems to find this worrying. First I got him to do a square, which he now does quite easily, then to join up the opposite corners within the square. He cannot seem to head straight for the opposite corner, but instead his pencil wanders about, wanting to go either vertically or horizontally. After practising for a time he got the diagonals within the square more or less right, although the lines were a bit wobbly. I then went on to try getting him to copy a triangle. Sam was completely thrown by this. He became very upset and swept his book to the floor. When he had settled again I tried to take him back to the previous stage of what we had been doing, but this proved to be impossible. He could no longer draw the lines within a square, nor could he even manage a square on its own. After doing just two sides of the figure he dissolved it into a circle. This has made me realize that pushing Sam too far can cause him to regress several stages. Occasionally, though, I do get it right. Then I can see him gradually inching forward in tiny steps with the task that we are doing. It is a delicate balance between overstretching Sam and stretching him enough to pull him forward. It often feels as though we are standing still.

But at least I know that Sam can learn to do things, as long as the teaching situation is tailored to suit his very particular needs. He requires a cocktail of positive feedback, firmness and supportive eye contact which is not easy to mix. A fast, intuitive response is required to catch his flickering interest, and an ability to tune in to his singular view of the world. By Sam's age a child has normally developed the ability to cope easily with the fact that his experience of the world does not always fit exactly what he would like it to be. Most children can deal with new information, and thus are able to learn despite the fact that it is not precisely shaped to fit their particular mental state. They can bridge over the imperfect join, and continue to move forwards. An autistic child cannot do this. For him the fit must be exact. If his experience does not correlate with what he wants or expects to happen, he simply cuts himself off psychologically. Then the jarring non-fit does not affect him, because he does not feel it.

To help Sam move out of his frozen state of arrested development, I feel that it is necessary for somebody to understand his feelings and mirror his fears by 'thinking themselves into his mind'. By first of all joining with him, I have found that it is sometimes possible to edge him slowly forwards. But empathizing to the point of sharing an autistic child's anxieties can be an alarming experience. The world is a terrifying place when seen from the shifting perspective which I believe to be Sam's point of view. He has no real sense of his own identity, no centre of gravity, no safe home base to return to in times of danger. I find that identifying with Sam's feelings sometimes unleashes long-buried emotions from my own childhood, which makes it virtually impossible for me to remain objective in my dealings with him.

There is a world of difference between understanding what Sam needs and knowing how I want to treat him, and what actually happens between the two of us. This must be so for most mothers and their children, but for Sam the stakes for my getting it right are high. If I do not help him towards more normal functioning within the next few years he will never be able to cope alone in the world.

Yet despite constant setbacks and accumulating stresses, there is no doubt that Sam and I are moving forwards. The angry resentment that used to emanate from each of us is now much less in evidence. The cold empty silences that lay between us are beginning to be filled with my comments on our everyday lives and Sam's slowly increasing contributions to our dialogue.

Although his being older makes Sam more difficult to handle in some ways, we are much happier with each other than we used to be. I am more relaxed and manage things better, and he responds positively to my improved state of mind.

I will never know the extent to which Sam has been affected by decisions that I have made and the different therapies we have tried. I have wondered whether moving to the south of England might not have been better for us, to where there is undoubtedly more specialized help available – or whether I should have let Peter come back home, and tried to patch things up between us. How would Sam be today if I had not spent years doing holding therapy with him, or not come across Frances Tustin and psychotherapy?

Although I have always done what seemed best for Sam at the time, my ideas about autism have become more clearly defined over the years. Anything that is said to help autistic children interests me, but now I am better equipped to gauge the things useful for Sam.

I think that the extent to which a therapy or treatment succeeds in helping an autistic child is largely determined by the amount of psychological support it provides for him. Assuming that his present inability to cope with any stress stems from his failure to develop gradually the means of doing so in infancy, then such extra emotional support goes some way towards filling the gap that was then created.

This 'psychological holding' contrasts strongly with the treatment that was advocated by the holding therapist we relied upon for so many years. Forcing Sam to shout was an attempt to put him in touch with his feelings, but it did not give him what he needed more than anything else – solid support based upon a sound understanding of his psychological state. In fact far from helping autistic children, it seems to me that holding therapy makes heavy demands upon them. What a mother is encouraged to say during the therapy sessions is couched in terms of what she herself needs, rather than what her child requires. I was prompted to tell Sam that I wanted him to speak and to overcome his autistic symptoms so that I could get on with living a more normal life. He was expected to respond to the fact that I needed him to shout, or to speak, or to behave properly. I was therefore asking him to help me – a tall order for a non-communicating terrified child. Looking back I think that it was quite illogical to expect a person who had remained non-communicating despite the most fundamental of all human imperatives – survival – to speak or shout simply because his mother demanded it of him.

Giving useful assistance to a very withdrawn child means first of all reaching out to him, for he cannot advance on his own. This is my understanding of what a psychotherapist attempts to do. She catches the child's utterances – both verbal and as expressed through play – and she interprets them back to him. She cradles him psychologically in an attempt to simulate the type of feedback that was missing during the time when he could not cope adequately.

I think that any therapy that enhances a child's sense of his own self – whether by increasing his body awareness, helping him to gain confidence by acquiring skills, or by enabling him to come to terms with his emotional self – can be useful to him if presented in a way that makes it possible for him to use it. I would love Sam to have some sort of body-oriented therapy, or music therapy, or even speech therapy, which I think would now be useful to him.

But perhaps no therapy can help a child as much as mending the damaged relationship between him and his mother. Things went wrong for Sam right at the beginning of his life, when it consisted of little other than eating, sleeping and his relationship with me. That relationship floundered, and I think the best thing that could happen for him would be to have it repaired.

Yet if the mother-child relationship is the source of an autistic child's withdrawal, then it is obviously in need of quite drastic changes if he is to get back on to the rails of normal development. This is often simply not possible.

Then it may be that one or several key figures (family members, teachers, therapists) could be of fundamental importance in aiding the autistic child's recovery. A relationship with any of these people might open up a line of communication. This could provide the vital link between inner and outer reality – the bridge which the child may one day cross to reach the joy of shared understanding with another person. There is no way of knowing what we might eventually achieve, but my son and I have begun to build that bridge.

17

THE BEGINNING
AT LAST

I realized years ago that in order to help my son I must first of all help myself. The emotionally battered person that I was after separating from Peter was hardly fit to look after herself, let alone a severely autistic child. One of the best decisions I made at that time was to spend money on my own therapy, for while I learned to cope with my emotional problems my relationship with Sam improved. Now I have reached the stage where I can care properly for my child, but now Sam's needs are far greater than they were. 'Good enough mothering' is no longer good enough for him.

My involvement with Sam has grown and become more rewarding as we have each become happier within ourselves and with each other. Now we love being together but are restricted by circumstances. The day is almost over when I pick him up from school – by the time we get home it is evening and almost his bedtime. How ironic it seems. I remember with sadness the lost years, those far off days when we had all the time in the world and it seemed nothing more than a burden.

I do not often think back to the early part of Sam's life, but recently I had cause to do so. A close friend had just had her first baby. The very idea of going to see her made me nervous, for she was in the nursing home where I had been with Sam. Finally the time came when it seemed impossible to postpone my visit any longer. As I parked the car by the low modern building I remembered the day, now more than nine years ago, when I had emerged from that same building – my footsteps crunching on the icy snow, my apprehensive excitement as we manoeuvred the carrycot into the back seat of the car. I remembered walking along this same corridor, up and down, anxiously pacing. There was the telephone I had wept into, trying to explain to my sister how unhappy I felt. Then on through the door and past the television room. The women who sat there laughing and chatting about their babies on this day were probably not dissimilar to the group I had watched and listened to nine years ago. But how different they looked to me now. Just ordinary, friendly women. Back then I had believed them to be antagonistic, scornful, laughing at me because I was not married or because nobody came to visit me. They had probably not even noticed me.

Suddenly I saw my friend. There she sat on the bed, cradling her baby in her arms, forming the perfect circle depicted in so many paintings. Mother and child. As I took the baby from her my painful memories evaporated. It was like looking at a new-born infant for the very first time. Her minute hands were still tightly closed, but I saw how her eyes focused upon mine if she was held in just the right position. Her responses fascinated me, they seemed so clear, so easy to discern. She lay peacefully against my shoulder – her lips shaped to enclose the nipple which for her would materialize automatically, just as it should. This baby was lucky. Her parents loved her and wanted her. There was a space in their lives all ready for her to fill – she would have a good start in life.

I looked through the glass partition to the cubicle where Sam and I had lain, remembering the cloud of insecurity that had enveloped me there. How I envied my friend, surrounded as she was by cards and presents and love. I remembered my nightmares and the way I used to disturb the other mothers in the ward by waking up screaming. Surely somebody should have noticed that there was cause for concern in my behaviour, surely we should have been checked up on in some way. I remembered also the occasional moments of joy when I had looked at Sam – usually just after Peter had visited. And how at these times I used to position his transparent crib so that I could lie on my bed and gaze at him. It had never seemed to be in quite the right place – he was always just to one side of my line of vision. I used to feel a strange longing, as though for something that I knew I could not have. He seemed to be so very far away, beyond my reach, that perfect, tiny baby.

Watching my friend's infant sucking contentedly at her breast, I remembered the bad feeding pattern that we had established almost immediately, when Sam had refused to suck and I had felt guilty and tried to hide the fact. Then my panic at being told that I could go home, the worry that Peter would be late or would not turn up to fetch us, the inadequacy of Sam's going-home outfit compared with the soft, cosy knitted garments worn by the other babies.

Fortunately my friend did not notice my unhappy state of mind as I slipped away from her bedside, for she had several other visitors. Later that day when going through Sam's early photographs I thought about all that had happened, and wept. He looked so beautiful, it was like seeing him for the first time. I longed with a burning desire for that baby – the child to whom I had given birth but had never properly related, looked at but never really seen, fed and clothed but never nurtured. How could I not have noticed those hands reaching out to me? I marvelled at the sensitive, intelligent face gazing back from the page of my album, incredulous that I had not seen it that way at the time. Then we had been separated by my anxiety, which hung always between us like an invisible wall. It hurt to think of the child that I had held so unknowingly in my arms, and I was filled with an overwhelming desire to love and care for him as I would now be able to do.

That painful journey back through ten years was the very first time that I had confronted my memory of my son's first weeks of life. In doing so I felt a scalded skinless thing, defenceless against the horror of what I was seeing. The unhappiness of my past seemed to merge with the loneliness of what must surely be Sam's future. He was utterly helpless, and is still so, only now he suffers from a continuous underlying terror of annihilation, a chronic fear which sometimes erupts into a more acute manifestation. He is like my own self when I was a child, but much, much worse. I did not visit my friend and her baby in hospital again; I could not bear to see them together. Her child had so much love, and mine had had so little. To be reminded of the vulnerable infant that Sam had been, so full of potential, and to know what had happened to him in the intervening years, just made me feel sick.

I hated all the people who I felt had contributed to the sad result that was my son. Peter for his emotional cruelty and for his violence, for punishing me for having a child and for making me feel guilty every time that I looked at Sam. My sisters for never coming near me when I so needed help, and for treating my son as though he did not exist. My mother I hated too, although she was long dead, for I felt she had never loved me, and had given me no experience of love or caring to pass on to my own child. But eventually I came to see that hate is futile. People live the drama of their own lives without setting out to hurt each other, but yet doing so constantly.

I thought how much better Sam's life might have been if only one of a number of things had been different. My relationship with Peter was never stable, but Sam's birth introduced an element with which we were unable to cope. If we had been less neurotically dependent on each other we might have drifted apart after Sam was born. Our son would then at least have had more emotional space in which to grow, and would not have been trapped at the centre of our battlefield. If either one of us had been able to stand back and view our situation more objectively, we might have seen the disastrous effect that our emotional upheavals were having on Sam. If we had had any support, or indeed any contact with relatives or friends, we might not have been so obsessively involved with each other. Even having more money would have helped, for during those first few years of Sam's life we were in a state of constant anxiety about the lack of it. And finally, I think that Sam would have suffered less if Peter and I had been less shrewd, as although on one level we were ashamed and frightened of our inability to look after our child, we manipulated situations in order to hide our real problems from the various professionals we encountered. This prevented us from getting the kind of help that we needed and unconsciously wanted.

But now I no longer feel hopeless and flattened by past events, for I realize all is not lost. I still have my son, and I love him dearly. Although Sam represents the unwanted child that I was (and in some ways still am) he is no longer unwanted, since I have become emotionally strong enough to understand and modify some of my initial responses to him. He is much damaged, but he is alive, and so am I. And in a strange way I feel that the harm which befell me as a child can be to some extent negated by helping my son towards a more normal life.

Today Sam is ten years old. He has been having psychotherapy for almost three years. Although he has improved, he is a very long way from being cured. But I am still hopeful. I am a very optimistic person – some might say a fool. Even so, I do not hope, as I once did, for a magical cure. I understand the crippling extent of my son's handicap. On the road that leads to development of an integrated personality he is only at the very beginning. And his childhood – the time when this development should be expanded and built upon – has almost gone.

During the past few years I have gradually realized that in our situation I could do little more than keep Sam ticking over, hoping always that in the future I might have the resources to give him the more intensive help that he needs. Perhaps it is still not too late for him. Perhaps autism is the living manifestation of man's age-old dream of being able to exist in a state of suspended animation, where the body waits for the time when its environment will improve so that a normal relationship with it can be resumed. The help that Sam would require to do this is not available where we live. I have always known that eventually we would have to move to the south. Until recently this seemed too daunting a prospect to contemplate. But now I am planning to make this move, for I want to simplify our disjointed lives. I want specialist schooling for Sam and I want to be nearer to his therapist, for Sam will be needing as much psychotherapy as I can afford for a very long time.

My son and I have come a long way together – through silent, cold detachment, to fearful erratic connections with each other, then to the formation of a more resilient bond and eventually to something that could truly be described as love. Nothing earth-shattering (although it often seems that way to me); just ordinary love that is based upon the bond between mother and child which so many people take for granted. I feel that we have at last arrived at the beginning of our relationship.

The last ten years have been interesting, but difficult, and I wish I could have learned the things I have learned in some easier way. I wish my life could have been different, and Sam not hurt or his personality distorted in the way that it is. More than anything, I wish I could go back to that bitter cold day in Valley View, when I drank champagne, and listened to Delius, and naïvely hoped that everything would be all right. I wish I could do it all again, and do it differently. I believe that if I could, my son would not be autistic.

EPILOGUE

Sam and I moved down to Oxford about nine months after I finished writing this book. It was hard tearing him away from everything that he knew, and impossible to predict how the changes in his life would affect him. And there is no doubt that leaving Yorkshire, his school and our house (which he loved) did disturb Sam. The changes upset us both. For months after our arrival here we used to wander around the new house feeling desolate. Sam developed an obsession about things being lost. He would think of some object, something quite arbitrary it might seem to me, and then become absolutely desperate until he was able to find it. This obsession still persists today, almost a year later.

But despite the problems that have resulted from uprooting and replanting ourselves, I am not sorry that we moved. Life is easier for us here. Sam has psychotherapy twice a week instead of only once, and it is in Oxford, so we no longer have to travel to London. He has a place in the autistic unit of the school that I wanted for him, which is also in Oxford, so now the things he needs are all here in the same town. I feel as though the strands of our lives are gradually drawing together.

There is still no way of knowing how much Sam will improve, and I still vacillate between unrestrained optimism and abject pessimism when thinking about what the future may hold for him. I want so much for Sam, and there are so many things that I know would help him. Unfortunately I am limited by the resources that are available, and by my own humanity. But Sam is now in the best situation that I can provide for him – for the moment at least. For the future we must wait and see.

BIBLIOGRAPHY

Attachment (Volume I of *Attachment and Loss*), John Bowlby, Penguin 1981 (1971).

Autism: Explaining the Enigma, Uta Frith, Basil Blackwell 1989.

Autism and Childhood Psychosis, Frances Tustin, Hogarth Press 1974.

Autistic Barriers in Neurotic Patients, Frances Tustin, Karnac Books 1986.

Autistic Children: A Guide for Parents, Lorna Wing, Constable 1971.

Autistic Children – New Hope for a Cure, Niko Tinbergen FRS and Elisabeth A. Tinbergen, Allen and Unwin 1983.

Autistic States in Children, Frances Tustin, Routledge and Kegan Paul 1981.

Boundary and Space: An Introduction to the Work of D.W. Winnicott, Madeleine Davis and David Wallbridge, Penguin 1981.

The Child, the Family and the Outside World, D.W. Winnicott, Penguin 1985 (1964).

Children Under Stress, Sula Wolff, Penguin 1983 (1969).

Dibs: In Search of Self, Virginia Axline, Penguin 1980 (1964).

The Drama of the Gifted Child and the Search for the True Self, Alice Miller, Faber and Faber 1983.

Early Childhood Autism, ed. Lorna Wing, Pergamon Press 1976.

The Empty Fortress, Bruno Bettelheim, Free Press 1972.

For the Love of Ann, James Copeland (based on a diary by Jack Hodges), Arrow 1976.

For Your Own Good, Alice Miller, Faber and Faber 1983.

In a Summer Garment, Ann Lovell, Secker and Warburg 1978.
The Riddle of Autism, George Victor, D.C. Heath 1983.
The Siege, Clara Clairborne Park, Hutchinson 1983 (1967).
The Silent Twins, Marjorie Wallace, Penguin 1986.
To Love is to be Happy with, Barry Neil Kaufman, Souvenir Press 1976.
Toys and Playthings, John and Elizabeth Newson, Penguin 1979.
Truants from Life, Bruno Bettelheim, Free Press 1964.
Why Your Child is Hyperactive, Ben F. Feingold, Random House 1975.